Book D

LANGUAGE

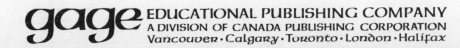
EDUCATIONAL PUBLISHING COMPANY
A DIVISION OF CANADA PUBLISHING CORPORATION
Vancouver · Calgary · Toronto · London · Halifax

Editorial Team: Chelsea Donaldson, Carol Waldock
Cover Adaptation: Christine Dandurand

ISBN **0-7715-1016-0**

2 3 4 5 MP 01 00 99 98 97
Printed and bound in Canada

Table of Contents

Unit 5 — Composition

Unit 6 — Study Skills

Final Reviews

Synonyms and Antonyms

> - A **synonym** is a word that has the same or nearly the same meaning as one or more other words.
>   EXAMPLES: joy – happiness   choose – pick

A. Write a synonym for each word below.

1. small _____
2. swiftly _____
3. weary _____
4. pretty _____

5. large _____
6. awful _____
7. lad _____
8. forest _____

9. cry _____
10. leap _____
11. wealthy _____
12. ugly _____

B. Circle the word in parentheses that is a synonym for the underlined word in each sentence.

1. (finish, begin)   When you <u>start</u> to write, think about your audience.
2. (fall, spring)   The colours of <u>autumn</u> leaves are breathtaking.
3. (sick, well)   Last week I was <u>ill</u> with the flu.
4. (tried, tired)   He was <u>exhausted</u> after the marathon.
5. (clothes, close)   I tried to <u>shut</u> the door, but it was stuck.

> - An **antonym** is a word that has the opposite meaning of another word
>   EXAMPLES: hot – cold   late – early

C. Write an antonym for each word below.

1. good _____
2. old _____
3. dull _____
4. thick _____

5. tall _____
6. crooked _____
7. happy _____
8. remember _____

9. ugly _____
10. near _____
11. obey _____
12. rich _____

D. Circle the word in parentheses that is an antonym for the underlined word in each sentence.

1. (heavy, hard)   The donkey strained under its <u>light</u> load.
2. (last, late)   The <u>early</u> morning sun streamed in the window.
3. (fine, kind)   Jerry gave the dog a <u>mean</u> pat on the head.
4. (empty, old)   I tried to pour some milk, but the carton was <u>full</u>.
5. (frowned, found)   Isabel <u>lost</u> her favourite book.

Lesson 2

Homonyms

> ■ A **homonym** is a word that sounds the same as another word but has a different spelling and a different meaning.
>
> EXAMPLES: to – two – too   sum – some

A. Underline the correct homonym(s) in each sentence below.

1. The couple walked for a mile along the (beech, beach).

2. Are there any (dear, deer) in these hills?

3. How much do you (way, weigh)?

4. Who broke this window (pane, pain)?

5. I have (to, too, two) go (to, too, two) the sale with those (to, too, two) people.

6. Laurie (knew, new) how to play a (new, knew) word game.

7. Juan and Luis spent a week at (there, their) friends' ranch.

8. Those boys (ate, eight) (ate, eight) of the apples we had just bought.

9. I like to walk by the (see, sea) at dusk.

10. (Wring, Ring) the bell, Matt.

11. Did you see what she brought (hear, here)?

12. He cannot (write, right) with his (write, right) hand.

13. Who has not (read, red) the magazine?

14. He found it cheaper to (buy, by) his pencils (buy, by) the box.

15. Chris told his niece a fairy (tale, tail).

B. Write a homonym for each word below.

1. hall _____	11. flower _____	21. our _____
2. threw _____	12. stair _____	22. sea _____
3. weak _____	13. pale _____	23. right _____
4. there _____	14. ring _____	24. peace _____
5. heard _____	15. soar _____	25. no _____
6. here _____	16. sale _____	26. grate _____
7. by _____	17. won _____	27. way _____
8. pane _____	18. aisle _____	28. cent _____
9. heal _____	19. rode _____	29. sew _____
10. blew _____	20. meet _____	30. forth _____

Unit 1, Vocabulary

Lesson 3

Homographs

> ■ A **homograph** is a word that has the same spelling as another word but a different meaning and sometimes a different pronunciation.
> EXAMPLE: <u>bow</u>, meaning "to bend the upper part of the body forward in respect," and <u>bow</u>, meaning "a weapon for shooting arrows"

vault   bore   interest

A. Fill in each blank with a homograph from the box. Use each homograph twice.

1. I won't _____ you by repeating the story again.

2. She looked with great _____ at the painting.

3. He used a long pole to _____ over the jump.

4. My savings account pays _____ on the money I keep in it.

5. Olaf keeps his stamp collection locked in a _____ .

6. Estelle used a special drill to _____ a hole in the concrete wall.

B. Circle the letter of the correct definition for each underlined homograph. Then write a sentence using the other meaning of the homograph.

1. Put your coins in the <u>bank</u>.

    a. a place where people save money   **b.** the ground along a river

    _____

2. If you <u>hide</u> your piggy bank, be sure to remember where you put it.

    a. keep out of sight   **b.** the skin of an animal

    _____

3. Some people keep their money in a <u>safe</u>.

    a. a metal box with a lock   **b.** free from danger

    _____

4. There are only two people who have the <u>key</u> to open the safe.

    a. a piece of metal to open a lock   **b.** a low island or reef

    _____

5. Many people have an <u>account</u> at a bank.

    a. explanation   **b.** an amount of money

    _____

Lesson 4
Prefixes

- A **prefix** added to the beginning of a base word changes the meaning of the word.
  - EXAMPLE: <u>un-</u>, meaning "not," + the base word <u>done</u> = <u>undone</u>, meaning "not done"
- Some prefixes have one meaning, and others have more than one meaning.

  EXAMPLES:

prefix	meaning
im-, in-, non-, un-	not
dis-, in-, non-	opposite of, lack of, not
mis-	bad, badly, wrong, wrongly
pre-	before
re-	again

A. Add the prefix <u>un-</u>, <u>im-</u>, <u>non-</u>, or <u>mis-</u> to the base word in parentheses. Write the new word in the sentence. Then write the definition of the new word on the line after the sentence. Use a dictionary if necessary.

1. It is _____ (practical) to put a new monkey into a cage with other monkeys.

   _____

2. The monkeys might _____ (behave) with a newcomer among them.

   _____

3. They will also feel quite _____ (easy) for a number of days or even weeks.

   _____

4. Even if the new monkey is _____ (violent) in nature, the others may harm it.

   _____

5. Sometimes animal behaviour can be quite _____ (usual).

   _____

B. Underline each prefix. Write the meaning of each word that has a prefix.

1. unexpected guest _____
2. really disappear _____
3. disagree often _____
4. misspell a name _____
5. preview a movie _____
6. reenter a room _____
7. misplace a shoe _____
8. impossible situation _____
9. nonstop reading _____
10. unimportant discussion _____
11. insane story _____
12. prejudge a person _____

   Unit 1, Vocabulary

Lesson 5

Suffixes

> ■ A **suffix** added to the end of a base word changes the meaning of the word.
> EXAMPLE: -ful meaning "full of," + the base word <u>joy</u> = <u>joyful</u>, meaning "full of joy"
> ■ Some **suffixes** have one meaning, and others have more than one meaning.
>
> | EXAMPLES: | suffix | meaning |
> |---|---|---|
> | | -able | able to be, suitable or inclined to |
> | | -al | relating to, like |
> | | -ful | as much as will fill, full of |
> | | -less | without, that does not |
> | | -ous | full of |
> | | -y | having, full of |

A. Add a suffix from the list above to the base word in parentheses. Write the new word. Then write the definition of the new word on the line after the sentence. Do not use any suffix more than once.

1. Switzerland is a _____ country. (mountain)

   _____

2. If you visit there, it is _____ to have a walking stick. (help)

   _____

3. Many tourists visit the country's _____ mountains to ski each year. (snow)

   _____

4. The Swiss people have a great deal of _____ pride. (nation)

   _____

5. Many Swiss are _____ about their country. (knowledge)

   _____

B. Underline each suffix. Write the meaning of each word that has a suffix.

1. breakable toy _____

2. endless waves _____

3. hazardous path _____

4. inflatable raft _____

5. poisonous snake _____

6. dependable trains _____

7. humorous program _____

8. tearful goodbye _____

9. bumpy ride _____

10. careless driver _____

11. natural food _____

12. magical appearance _____

Lesson 6

Contractions

- A **contraction** is a word formed by joining two other words.
- An **apostrophe** shows where a letter or letters have been left out.
  EXAMPLE: do not = don't
- Won't is an exception.
  EXAMPLE: will not = won't

A. Underline each contraction. Write the words that make up each contraction on the line.

1. Stingrays look as if they're part bird, part fish. _____

2. Stingrays cover themselves with sand so they won't be seen. _____

3. There's a chance that waders might step on a stingray and get stung. _____

4. That's a painful way to learn that you shouldn't forget about stingrays.

   _____   _____

5. Until recently, stingrays weren't seen very often. _____

6. It doesn't seem likely, but some stingrays will eat out of divers' hands. _____

7. Because its mouth is underneath, the stingray can't see what it's eating.

   _____   _____

8. Once they've been fed by hand, they'll flutter around for more.

   _____   _____

9. It's hard to believe these stingrays aren't afraid of the divers.

   _____   _____

10. To pet a stingray, they'd gently touch its velvety skin. _____

B. Find the pairs of words that can be made into contractions. Underline each pair. Then write the contraction each word pair can make on the lines following the sentences.

1. I have never tried scuba diving, but I would like to.

   _____   _____

2. It is a good way to explore what is under the water.

   _____   _____

3. First, I will need to take lessons in the pool. _____

4. Then I can find out what to do if the equipment does not work. _____

                                    Unit 1, Vocabulary

Compound Words

> - A **compound word** is a word that is made up of two or more words. The meaning of a compound word is related to the meaning of each individual word.
>   - EXAMPLE: sun + glasses = sunglasses, meaning "glasses to wear in the sun"
> - Compound words may be written as one word, as hyphenated words, or as two separate words.
>   - EXAMPLES: highway   out-patient   high school

A. Answer the following questions.

1. Something that has sharp, curved points extending backward is said to be <u>barbed</u>.

   What is <u>barbed wire</u>? _____

2. <u>Dry</u> means "without water." What does <u>dry-clean</u> mean? _____

3. <u>Head</u> means "a heading." What is a <u>headline</u>? _____

4. A <u>deputy</u> is "a person appointed to take the place of another."

   What is a <u>deputy minister</u>? _____

5. <u>Bare</u> means "without a covering." What does <u>bareback</u> mean? _____

6. A <u>way</u> is a route. What is a <u>railway</u>? _____

7. A <u>paper</u> is a type of document. What is a <u>newspaper</u>? _____

8. <u>Blue</u> is a colour. What is a <u>blueberry</u>? _____

B. Combine words from the box to make compound words. Use the compound words to complete the sentences. You will use one word twice.

cut	every	fore	hair	head	where
loud	news	speaker	stand	thing	

1. Bob's hair covered his _____ .

2. He knew it was time to get a _____ .

3. He saw a truck hit a fire hydrant, which sprayed water _____ .

4. The corner _____ was soaked.

5. A police officer used a _____ to direct traffic.

6. It was so exciting, Bob forgot about _____ , including his haircut!

Lesson 8

Connotation/Denotation

- The **denotation** of a word is its exact meaning as stated in a dictionary.
  - EXAMPLE: The denotation of <u>skinny</u> is "very thin."
- The **connotation** of a word is an added meaning that suggests something positive or negative.
  - EXAMPLES: **Negative:** <u>Skinny</u> suggests "too thin." Skinny has a negative connotation.
  - **Positive:** <u>Slender</u> suggests "attractively thin." Slender has a positive connotation.
- Some words are neutral. They do not suggest either good or bad feelings.
  - EXAMPLES: month, building, chair

A. Underline the word in parentheses that has the more positive connotation.

1. Our trip to the amusement park was (fine, wonderful).

2. (Brave, Foolhardy) people rode on the roller coaster.

3. We saw (fascinating, weird) animals in the animal house.

4. Some of the monkeys made (hilarious, amusing) faces.

5. Everyone had a (smile, smirk) on his or her face on the way home.

B. Underline the word in parentheses that has the more negative connotation.

1. We bought (cheap, inexpensive) souvenirs at the amusement park.

2. I ate a (soggy, moist) sandwich.

3. Mike (nagged, reminded) us to go to the fun house.

4. The fun house was (comical, silly).

5. I didn't like the (smirk, grin) on the jester's face.

6. It made me feel (uneasy, frightened).

C. Answer the following questions.

1. Which is worth more, something <u>old</u> or something <u>antique</u>? _____

2. Is it better to be <u>slender</u> or to be <u>skinny</u>?_____

3. Which would you rather be called, <u>thrifty</u> or <u>cheap</u>? _____

4. Would a vain person be more likely to <u>stroll</u> or to <u>parade</u>? _____

5. Which is more serious, a <u>problem</u> or a <u>disaster</u>? _____

6. Is it more polite to <u>sip</u> a drink or to <u>gulp</u> it? _____

7. If you hadn't eaten for days, would you be <u>hungry</u> or <u>starving</u>? _____

8. After walking in mud, would your shoes be <u>dirty</u> or <u>filthy</u>? _____

 Unit 1, Vocabulary

Idioms

- An **idiom** is an expression that has a meaning different from the usual meanings of the individual words within it.
  EXAMPLE: <u>To lend a hand</u> means "to help," not "to loan someone a hand."

A. Match the idioms underlined in the sentences below with their meanings. Write the correct letter on each line.

a. in a risky situation   **f.** continue to have hope

b. do less than I should   **g.** listen with all your attention

c. admit having said the wrong thing   **h.** teasing

d. play music after only hearing it   **i.** accept defeat

e. spend money carefully   **j.** meet by chance

_____ 1. I had hoped to <u>run across</u> some old friends at the ball game.

_____ 2. Their team was ready to <u>throw in the towel</u> when we scored our tenth run!

_____ 3. Peggy was <u>pulling my leg</u> when she told me that there are koalas in Africa.

_____ 4. I told her that she was <u>skating on thin ice</u> when she tried to trick me.

_____ 5. My sister must <u>make ends meet</u> with the little money she has for university.

_____ 6. I told her, "Always <u>keep your chin up</u> when things get difficult."

_____ 7. Dinesh can <u>play by ear</u> the theme songs to all his favourite movies.

_____ 8. If you don't believe me, just <u>be all ears</u> when he plays.

_____ 9. My brother said that I would <u>lie down on the job</u> if he weren't watching over me.

_____ 10. I told Bill that he would <u>eat his words</u> once he saw how much work I had done.

B. Underline the idioms in the following sentences. On the line after each sentence, explain what the idiom means. Use a dictionary if necessary.

1. Frank was in hot water when he arrived late.

   _____

2. His friends were beside themselves with worry.

   _____

3. Frank told them not to fly off the handle.

   _____

4. His friends explained that they had been shaken up.

   _____

5. They all decided to sit down and talk turkey.

   _____

Review

A. Write a synonym and an antonym for each underlined word below.

1. a <u>pleasant</u> trip _____ _____

2. to <u>increase</u> speed _____ _____

3. an <u>awful</u> mistake _____ _____

4. a <u>funny</u> joke _____ _____

5. a <u>correct</u> answer _____ _____

6. a <u>dangerous</u> stunt _____ _____

B. Underline the correct homonyms in each sentence below.

1. If you go by (plane, plain), you'll arrive (there, their) more quickly than by bus.

2. A bus could take a (weak, week), but you'll get (to, too, two) (see, sea) more.

3. If you couldn't (bear, bare) a long trip, an overnight trip (wood, would) do instead.

4. An overnight trip can be (cheep, cheap), relaxing, and a nice (break, brake) in your busy (week, weak).

C. Circle the letter of the correct definition for each underlined homograph. Then write a sentence using the other meaning of the homograph.

1. If you like to feel the <u>wind</u> in your hair, you might like sailing.

   a. moving air   **b.** to wrap in a circle

   _____

2. A sailboat will often <u>heel</u> if the sails are tight and the winds are strong.

   a. the rounded back part of the foot   **b.** lean to one side

   _____

3. It should only take a <u>minute</u> to complete the survey.

   a. a time period of sixty seconds   **b.** extremely small

   _____

4. Our city has had a <u>rash</u> of burglaries in the last two weeks.

   a. a skin problem   **b.** an outbreak of incidents within a short time period

   _____

D. Underline the prefix in each phrase below. Then write the meaning of each word that has the prefix.

1. impossible problem _____

2. incomplete work _____

3. uneasy feeling _____

4. nonviolent protest _____

5. disinterested student _____

6. refurnish a house _____

7. mispronounce a word _____

8. prehistoric animal _____

E. Underline the suffix in each phrase below. Then write the meaning of each word that has the suffix.

1. hazardous road _____

2. helpless kitten _____

3. profitable business _____

4. regional finals _____

F. Write the contraction each word pair can make.

1. we will _____

2. she would _____

3. will not _____

4. they have _____

5. you will _____

6. we are _____

G. Combine words from the box to make compound words. Use the compound words to complete the sentences.

| road table sand snow plough cross lot top |

1. When we came to the _____ , we turned right.

2. The children played football in the _____ .

3. Tim needed a _____ to clear the road to the highway.

4. The family photograph on the _____ was nicely framed.

H. For each pair of phrases below, write the underlined word that has a positive connotation.

_____ 1. **a.** cheap material   **b.** inexpensive material

_____ 2. **a.** cosy apartment   **b.** cramped apartment

_____ 3. **a.** curious neighbour   **b.** nosy neighbour

_____ 4. **a.** lazy dog   **b.** relaxed dog

I. Underline the idiom in each of the following sentences. On the line after the sentence, explain what the idiom means.

1. You should stay on your toes while driving a car.

_____

2. If you run across a friend, stop and talk.

_____

3. Eileen saw red when she noticed graffiti on her new fence.

_____

4. When Sarah gave her speech, the audience was all ears.

_____

A. Rewrite the following sentences, using synonyms for the underlined words.

1. The lightning flashed across the <u>black</u> sky as the trees <u>bent</u> in the wind.

   _____

2. <u>Blasts</u> of wind whistled through the <u>openings</u> between the boards on the window.

   _____

3. Then a <u>hush</u> seemed to fall over our part of the <u>world</u>.

   _____

B. Rewrite the following sentences, using antonyms for the underlined words.

1. <u>Before</u> the storm hit, the sky got <u>darker</u>.

   _____

2. <u>Black</u> clouds drifted across the <u>evening</u> sky.

   _____

3. The <u>heavy</u> wind was blowing leaves <u>over</u> the trees.

   _____

C. Write a sentence using a homonym for each word.

1. new _____

2. grater _____

3. choose _____

4. weight _____

5. waist _____

D. For each homograph below, write two sentences. Be sure to use a different meaning of the homograph in each sentence.

1. light a. _____

           b. _____

2. shed a. _____

           b. _____

3. rest a. _____

           b. _____

E. Add one of the following prefixes or suffixes to each base word to make a new word.

> **Prefixes:** in-, non-, dis-, mis-, pre-, re-
> **Suffixes:** -able, -ful, -less

1. place _____
2. direct _____
3. use _____
4. measure _____
5. speech _____

6. tire _____
7. remark _____
8. spell _____
9. pay _____
10. fund _____

F. Use the following idioms in sentences. Use a dictionary if necessary.

1. throw in the towel _____
2. pulling my leg _____
3. skating on thin ice _____
4. get in touch with _____
5. keep an eye on _____

G. Think of words that have almost the same meaning as the neutral word, but have a more negative or positive connotation. Complete the chart with your words.

Negative Connotation	Neutral	Positive Connotation
1. _____	wet	_____
2. _____	shout	_____
3. _____	thin	_____
4. _____	old	_____
5. _____	talk	_____
6. _____	clothes	_____
7. _____	ask	_____
8. _____	work	_____
9. _____	cut	_____
10. _____	eat	_____

- A **sentence** is a group of words that expresses a complete thought.
  EXAMPLE: Marie sings well.

- **Some of the following groups of words are sentences, and some are not. Write S before each group that is a sentence. Punctuate each sentence with a period.**

_____ 1. When the downhill skiing season begins _____

_____ 2. Last summer I visited my friend in New Jersey _____

_____ 3. From the very beginning of the first-aid lessons _____

_____ 4. One of the children from the neighbourhood _____

_____ 5. A visiting musician played the organ _____

_____ 6. On the way to school this morning _____

_____ 7. "I love you, Mother," said Mike _____

_____ 8. The blue house at the corner of Maple Street _____

_____ 9. After Hermia left, the phone rang off the hook _____

_____ 10. Speak distinctly and loudly so that you can be heard _____

_____ 11. I have finally learned to drive our car _____

_____ 12. This is William's tenth birthday _____

_____ 13. At the very last moment, we were ready _____

_____ 14. When you speak in front of people _____

_____ 15. The basket of fruit on the table _____

_____ 16. Please answer the telephone, Julia _____

_____ 17. Hurrying to class because he is late _____

_____ 18. The first thing in the morning _____

_____ 19. That mistake was costly and unfortunate _____

_____ 20. We are planning to build a new doghouse _____

_____ 21. The dog chased the cat up the tree _____

_____ 22. Joni Mitchell was born in Alberta _____

_____ 23. The giant maple in our backyard _____

_____ 24. Maria, bring my notebook _____

_____ 25. On a stool beside the back door _____

_____ 26. Sometimes the noise from the street _____

_____ 27. Somewhere out of the province _____

_____ 28. The band played a lively march _____

_____ 29. That flight arrived on time _____

_____ 30. Was cracked in dozens of places _____

- A **declarative** sentence makes a statement. It is followed by a period (.).
   EXAMPLES: It is warm today. I took off my coat.
- An **interrogative** sentence asks a question. It is followed by a question mark (?).
   EXAMPLES: When is Tony coming? Why is the bus late today?

- **Write D before each declarative sentence and IN before each interrogative sentence. Put the correct punctuation mark at the end of the sentence.**

_____IN_____ 1. Who is your favourite author ____?____

_____ 2. How are our forests protected from fire _____

_____ 3. Tim learned the names of the trees in his neighbourhood _____

_____ 4. A good driver obeys every traffic law _____

_____ 5. The hippopotamus lives in Africa _____

_____ 6. Do you know the legend of the dogwood tree _____

_____ 7. Every sentence should begin with a capital letter _____

_____ 8. Ryan is repairing the lamp _____

_____ 9. Did you ever see a kangaroo _____

_____ 10. Where did these fragrant roses grow _____

_____ 11. Beautiful furniture can be made from the oak tree _____

_____ 12. Flour can be made from dried bananas _____

_____ 13. Did anyone find Pascal's book _____

_____ 14. Andrea feeds the goldfish every day _____

_____ 15. How many people are studying to be pilots _____

_____ 16. Kelly is going to the show with us _____

_____ 17. Last summer we made a trip to Cape Breton _____

_____ 18. How old are you _____

_____ 19. The architect and her assistant inspected the building _____

_____ 20. When did you arrive at the meeting _____

_____ 21. Did you forget your wallet _____

_____ 22. That light bulb is burned out _____

_____ 23. The baby crawled across the room _____

_____ 24. When would you like to eat _____

_____ 25. Mariko helped Andy wash the car _____

_____ 26. Did they wax the car _____

_____ 27. How did you make that sand castle _____

_____ 28. It is easy to make if we work together _____

More Types of Sentences

- An **imperative** sentence expresses a command or a request. It is followed by a period (.).   EXAMPLE: Close the door.
- An **exclamatory** sentence expresses strong or sudden feeling. It is followed by an exclamation point (!).   EXAMPLE: I am innocent!

- **Write IM before each imperative sentence and E before each exclamatory sentence. Put the correct punctuation mark at the end of each sentence.**

__IM__	**1.**	Write the names of the days of the week _____ .
_____	**2.**	Please mail this package for me _____
_____	**3.**	I love the gift you gave me _____
_____	**4.**	Lay the papers on the desk _____
_____	**5.**	How beautiful the night is _____
_____	**6.**	Watch out for that turning car _____
_____	**7.**	Drive more slowly _____
_____	**8.**	Keep time with the music _____
_____	**9.**	Deliver this message immediately _____
_____	**10.**	Sign your name in my yearbook _____
_____	**11.**	That airplane is so huge _____
_____	**12.**	Please lend me a postage stamp _____
_____	**13.**	I'm delighted with the flowers _____
_____	**14.**	How blue the sky is _____
_____	**15.**	My neighbour's shed is on fire _____
_____	**16.**	The baby's lip is bleeding _____
_____	**17.**	I can't believe that I got a perfect score _____
_____	**18.**	Pass the green beans _____
_____	**19.**	Write down these sentences _____
_____	**20.**	That movie was so exciting _____
_____	**21.**	The puppy is so playful _____
_____	**22.**	Look both ways when crossing the street _____
_____	**23.**	What a pretty red and blue sailboat _____
_____	**24.**	Please repeat what you said _____
_____	**25.**	Put the vase on the table _____
_____	**26.**	Be more careful with your work _____
_____	**27.**	That's a fantastic book to read _____
_____	**28.**	This is a wonderful surprise _____

- Every sentence has two main parts, a **complete subject** and a **complete predicate**.
- The complete subject includes all the words that tell who or what the sentence is about.
  EXAMPLES: **My brother**/likes to go with us. **Six geese**/honked loudly.
- The complete predicate includes all the words that state the action or condition of the subject.
  EXAMPLES: My brother/**likes to go with us**. Six geese/**honked loudly**.

- **Draw a line between the complete subject and the complete predicate in each sentence.**

1. Bees/fly.
2. Trains whistle.
3. A talented artist drew this cartoon.
4. The wind blew furiously.
5. My grandmother made this dress last year.
6. We surely have enjoyed the holiday.
7. These cookies are made with rice.
8. This letter came to the post office box
9. They rent a cabin in Muskoka every summer.
10. Jennifer is reading about the early days in Upper Canada.
11. Our hockey team won the third game of the playoffs.
12. The band played a cheerful tune.
13. A cloudless sky is a great help to a pilot.
14. The voice of the auctioneer was heard throughout the hall.
15. A sudden flash of lightning startled us.
16. The wind howled down the chimney.
17. Paul's dog followed him to the grocery store.
18. Their apartment is on the sixth floor.
19. We have studied many interesting places.
20. Each player on the team deserves credit for the victory.
21. Forest rangers fought the raging fire.
22. A friend taught Robert a valuable lesson.
23. Millions of stars make up the Milky Way.
24. The airplane was lost in the thick clouds.
25. Many of the children waded in the pool.
26. Terra Nova is a large national park.
27. Cold weather is predicted for tomorrow.
28. The trees were covered with moss.

Simple Subjects and Predicates

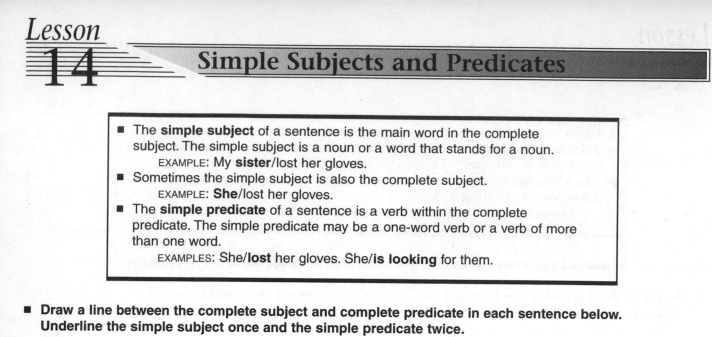

- The **simple subject** of a sentence is the main word in the complete subject. The simple subject is a noun or a word that stands for a noun.
    EXAMPLE: My **sister**/lost her gloves.
- Sometimes the simple subject is also the complete subject.
    EXAMPLE: **She**/lost her gloves.
- The **simple predicate** of a sentence is a verb within the complete predicate. The simple predicate may be a one-word verb or a verb of more than one word.
    EXAMPLES: She/**lost** her gloves. She/**is looking** for them.

■ **Draw a line between the complete subject and complete predicate in each sentence below. Underline the simple subject once and the simple predicate twice.**

1. A sudden <u>clap</u> of thunder/<u>frightened</u> all of us.

2. The soft snow covered the fields and roads.

3. We drove very slowly over the narrow bridge.

4. The students are making an aquarium.

5. Our class read about the founder of Hart House.

6. The women were talking in the park.

7. This album has many folk songs.

8. We are providing the sandwiches for tonight's picnic.

9. All the trees on that lawn are giant oaks.

10. Many Canadians are working in foreign countries.

11. The manager read the names of the contest winners.

12. Bill brought these large melons.

13. We opened the front door of the house.

14. The two mechanics worked on the car for an hour.

15. Black and yellow butterflies fluttered among the flowers.

16. The child spoke politely.

17. We found many beautiful shells along the shore.

18. The best part of the program is the dance number.

19. Every ambitious person is working hard.

20. Cheryl swam across the lake two times.

21. Our program will begin promptly at eight o'clock.

22. The handle of this basket is broken.

23. The clock in the tower strikes every hour.

24. The white farmhouse on that road belongs to my cousin.

25. The first game of the season will be played tomorrow.

Lesson 15

- When the subject of a sentence comes before all or part of the predicate, the sentence is in **natural order**.
  - EXAMPLE: The <u>puppy</u> <u>scampered</u> away.
- When all or part of the predicate comes before the subject, the sentence is in **inverted order**.
  - EXAMPLE: Away <u>scampered</u> the <u>puppy</u>.
- Many interrogative sentences are in inverted order.
  - EXAMPLE: Where <u>is</u> / <u>James</u>?

A. Draw a line between the complete subject and the complete predicate in each sentence. Write I in front of sentences that are in inverted order.

__I__	1.	Lightly falls/the mist.
_____	2.	The peaches on this tree are ripe now.
_____	3.	Over and over rolled the rocks.
_____	4.	Down the street marched the band.
_____	5.	Near the ocean are many birds.
_____	6.	Right under the chair ran the kitten.
_____	7.	He hit the ball a long way.
_____	8.	Along the ridge hiked the campers.
_____	9.	Underground is the stream.
_____	10.	The fish jumped in the lake.
_____	11.	Over the hill came the trucks.
_____	12.	Out came the rainbow.

B. Rewrite each inverted sentence in Exercise A in natural order.

1. _____

2. _____

3. _____

4. _____

5. _____

6. _____

7. _____

8. _____

9. _____

Using Compound Subjects

> ■ Two sentences in which the subjects are different but the predicates are the same can be combined into one sentence. The two subjects are joined by <u>and</u>. The subject of the new sentence is called a **compound subject**.
>
> EXAMPLE: **Lynn** visited an amusement park.
> **Eric** visited an amusement park.
> **Lynn** and **Eric** visited an amusement park.

A. Draw a line between the complete subject and the complete predicate in each sentence. If the subject is compound, write CS before the sentence.

_____CS_____ 1. English settlers and French settlers/came to Canada as early as the 1600s.

_____ 2. Trees and bushes were chopped down to make room for their houses.

_____ 3. The fierce winds and the cold temperatures made the first winters very harsh.

_____ 4. First Nations people helped the settlers grow food in the new country.

_____ 5. Potatoes and corn were first grown by First Nations people of North America.

_____ 6. English settlers and French settlers had never tasted turkey.

_____ 7. Peanuts and sunflower seeds are native North American foods that we now eat for snacks.

_____ 8. Kayaks and snowshoes helped the settlers to travel.

_____ 9. Many native medicines were useful to the new arrivals.

_____ 10. The First Nations people taught them how to survive in the new land.

B. Combine each pair of sentences below. Underline the compound subject.

1. Lumber from the New World was sent to Europe. Furs from the New World were sent to Europe.

_____

_____

2. Jacques Cartier wrote about his explorations. Samuel de Champlain wrote about his explorations.

_____

_____

3. John Cabot explored parts of North America. Henry Hudson explored parts of North America.

_____

_____

C. Write a sentence with a compound subject.

_____

■ Two sentences in which the subjects are the same but the predicates
are different can be combined into one sentence. The two predicates
may be joined by <u>or</u>, <u>and</u>, or <u>but</u>. The predicate of the new sentence is
sailed a **compound predicate**.

EXAMPLE: The crowd **cheered** the players.
The crowd **applauded** the players.
The crowd **cheered and applauded** the players.

A. **Draw a line between the complete subject and the complete predicate in each sentence.**
If the predicate is compound, write <u>CP</u> before the sentence.

_____ 1. The students organized a picnic for their families.

_____ 2. They discussed and chose a date for the picnic.

_____ 3. They wrote and designed invitations.

_____ 4. The invitations were mailed and delivered promptly.

5. Twenty-five families responded to the invitations.

_____ 6. The students bought the food and made the sandwiches.

_____ 7. The families bought the soft drinks.

_____ 8. The students packed and loaded the food into a truck.

_____ 9. The families brought and set up the volleyball nets.

_____ 10. Everyone participated in the games and races.

_____ 11. They ran relay races and threw water balloons.

_____ 12. Everyone packed the food and cleaned up the picnic area at the end of the day.

B. **Combine each pair of sentences below. Underline the compound predicate.**

1. Caroline heard the music. Caroline memorized the music.

_____

_____

2. Raja picked up the newspapers. Raja loaded the newspapers into his car.

_____

_____

3. Larry studied the names of the provinces. Larry wrote down the names of the provinces.

_____

_____

C. **Write a sentence with a compound predicate.**

_____

Simple and Compound Sentences

> ■ A **simple sentence** has one subject and one predicate.
>   EXAMPLE: The earth/is covered by land and water.
> ■ A **compound sentence** is made up of two simple sentences joined by a connecting word such as <u>and</u>, <u>but</u>, and <u>or</u>. A comma is placed before the connecting word.
>   EXAMPLE: One-fourth of the earth/is covered by land, and the land/is divided into seven continents.

A. Draw a line between the complete subject and the complete predicate in each sentence. Write <u>S</u> before each simple sentence. Write <u>C</u> before each compound sentence.

_____ 1. The seven continents of the world are North America, South America, Africa, Europe, Australia, Asia, and Antarctica.

_____ 2. Three-fourths of the earth is covered by water, and most of it is salty ocean water.

_____ 3. The four oceans of the world are the Pacific, the Atlantic, the Indian, and the Arctic.

_____ 4. We cannot exist without water, but we cannot drink the salty ocean water.

_____ 5. Most of the water we drink comes from lakes, rivers, and streams.

_____ 6. Clean water is a priceless resource.

B. Combine each pair of simple sentences below into a compound sentence.

1. The Pacific Ocean is the largest ocean in the world.
   It covers more area than all the earth's land put together.

   _____

   _____

2. Bodies of salt water that are smaller than oceans are called seas, gulfs, or bays.
   These bodies of water are often encircled by land.

   _____

   _____

3. Seas, gulfs, and bays are joined to the oceans.
   They vary in size and depth.

   _____

   _____

4. The Mediterranean is one of the earth's largest seas.
   It is almost entirely encircled by the southern part of Europe, the northern part of Africa, and the western part of Asia.

   _____

   _____

   _____

Correcting Run-on Sentences

> - Two or more sentences run together without the correct punctuation are called a **run-on sentence**.
>   - EXAMPLE: It will rain today, tomorrow the sun will shine.
> - One way to correct a run-on sentence is to separate it into two sentences.
>   - EXAMPLE: It will rain today. Tomorrow the sun will shine.
> - Another way to correct a run-on sentence is to separate the two main parts with a comma and <u>and</u>, <u>or</u>, <u>but</u>, <u>nor</u>, or <u>yet</u>.
>   - EXAMPLE: It will rain today, but tomorrow the sun will shine.

- **Rewrite each run-on sentence correctly.**

1. On December 6, 1817, two ships collided in Halifax harbour one was carrying a cargo of explosives.

   _____

   _____

2. Fifteen minutes after the collision, the cargo exploded, after the blast came a tidal wave.

   _____

   _____

3. A huge area of the city was flattened, six thousand people were left homeless in the middle of winter.

   _____

   _____

4. In all, more than 2 000 people died, many more were injured.

   _____

   _____

5. Relief supplies flooded in from other cities the total cost of the damages was $30 million.

   _____

   _____

6. Many acts of heroism were reported people helped each other to pull through.

   _____

   _____

■ Sentences can be **expanded** by adding details to make them clearer and more interesting.

EXAMPLE: The child waved. The child **in the blue hat** waved **timidly to me**.

■ Details added to sentences may answer these questions: When? (today) Where? (at home) How? (slowly) How often? (daily) To what degree? (very) What kind? (big) Which? (smallest) How many? (five)

A. Expand each sentence by adding details to answer the questions shown in parentheses. Write the expanded sentence on the line.

1. The ball soared. (What kind? Where?)

   _____

2. It crashed. (How? Where?)

   _____

3. It rolled. (When? Where?)

   _____

4. I felt. (How? To what degree?)

   _____

B. Decide how each of the following sentences can be expanded. Write your new sentence on the line.

1. The fires spread. _____

   _____

2. People ran. _____

   _____

3. Homes and trees blazed. _____

   _____

4. Firefighters came. _____

   _____

5. Water sprayed. _____

   _____

6. Flames died out. _____

   _____

A. Label each sentence as follows: Write <u>D</u> if it is declarative, <u>IN</u> if it is interrogative, <u>IM</u> if it is imperative, and <u>E</u> if it is exclamatory. Write <u>X</u> if the group of words is not a sentence. Punctuate each sentence correctly.

_____   1. What is your favourite radio station _____

_____   2. The one I listen to is having a contest _____

_____   3. Call this number to win a prize _____

_____   4. If you are the seventh caller _____

_____   5. The winner will be announced immediately _____

_____   6. I just won _____

_____   7. What did I win _____

_____   8. A trip to the Bahamas _____

_____   9. I'm so excited _____

_____   10. Who wants to go with me _____

B. Draw a line between the complete subject and the complete predicate in each sentence below. Underline the simple subject once. Underline the simple predicate twice.

1. You must guess the number of beans in the jar.

2. John will write his guesses on these pieces of paper.

3. His younger sister has already written her guess.

4. His twin brothers will write their guesses after school.

5. Each member of the family hopes to guess the winning number.

6. Only one person can win.

C. The sentences below are in inverted order. Rewrite each sentence in natural order.

1. In the mail came Maria's contest entry form. _____

_____

2. Right into the trash went her contestant prize number. _____

_____

3. In the city dump was buried the winning prize number. _____

_____

4. What she did Maria will never know. _____

_____

D. Label each sentence below as follows: Write <u>CS</u> if it has a compound subject, <u>CP</u> if it has a compound predicate, <u>C</u> if it is a compound sentence, and <u>R</u> if it is a run-on sentence.

_____ **1.** Contestants buy something and fill out a form.

_____ **2.** Rules and dates for a contest are often printed on the entry form.

_____ **3.** Some contests require contestants to create something some do not.

_____ **4.** I think of contests as challenging, and I often enter them.

_____ **5.** My brother and I created a jingle for one interesting contest.

_____ **6.** I wrote the words for the jingle, and my brother wrote the music.

_____ **7.** We made a tape of our jingle and mailed it in.

_____ **8.** Our jingle was the winning entry we were so excited.

E. Combine each pair of sentences below. Underline the compound subject or compound predicate.

1. Jan listened to the song playing on the radio. Paul listened to the song playing on the radio. _____

_____

2. They both knew the title of the song. They both remembered who recorded it. _____

_____

F. Combine each pair of simple sentences to make a compound sentence.

1. I enjoy entering recipe contests. My favourite contests are for dessert recipes. _____

_____

2. I create most of my recipes from scratch. I add unusual ingredients to existing recipes. _____

_____

G. Rewrite each run-on sentence correctly.

1. Many people win contests every day some people just have to write their names on an entry form to win.

_____

2. Some contest winners are given numbers, the winning prize numbers are drawn randomly. _____

_____

H. Expand the sentence below by inserting details. Write your expanded sentence on the blank lines.

1. The contest was won by a woman. _____

_____

A. Write complete sentences with each group of words below. In each sentence, underline the simple subject once and the simple predicate twice.

1. when I speak in front of people

   _____

2. the noise from the street

   _____

3. on the way to school this morning

   _____

4. a long way from home

   _____

5. had a birthday party for Diane

   _____

B. Complete each sentence below to make the kind of sentence named. Be sure to use the correct end punctuation.

1. **Declarative**   The solar system consists of   _____

2. **Interrogative**   Which is the largest   _____

3. **Imperative**   Tell the class   _____

4. **Exclamatory**   What an enormous   _____

C. To each compound subject or compound predicate below, add whatever words are needed to make a sentence.

1. _____ arrived at the game and sat in their seats.

2. _____ swept the plate and cried, "Play ball!"

3. The batter and the pitcher _____ .

4. _____ swung at and missed the ball.

5. The pitcher and the catcher _____ .

6. _____ hit the ball and ran the bases.

D. Write two sentences in inverted order.

   _____

   _____

E. Rewrite the sentences below, making one of these improvements: (a) combine sentences by using compound subjects or compound predicates; (b) combine simple sentences to make compound sentences; (c) correct run-on sentences.

1. To take a good photograph, you need a good eye you do not need an expensive camera.

   _____

   _____

2. You just load your camera then you go for a walk.

   _____

   _____

3. You may see something that is different. You may see something that is colourful.

   _____

   _____

4. Perhaps you like the shape of an object or maybe you like the texture of an object.

   _____

   _____

5. Don't take your picture yet be sure your lens cap is off and your camera is focussed correctly.

   _____

   _____

6. Think about what you do not want in your picture. Think about the way you want to frame your picture.

   _____

   _____

7. Take your time. Keep your camera steady.

   _____

   _____

F. Expand each sentence below by adding details that make it clearer and more interesting.

1. The traffic roars on the highway.

   _____

2. Cars move in and out of the lanes.

   _____

3. Trucks go past small cars.

   _____

  Unit 2, Sentences

> ■ A **noun** is a word that names a person, place, thing, or quality.
>   EXAMPLES: boy, Maria, river, New Brunswick, house, beach, joy

A. Write nouns that name the following:

1. Four famous people

   _____   _____

   _____   _____

2. Four types of jobs

   _____   _____

   _____   _____

3. Four places you would like to visit

   _____   _____

   _____   _____

4. Four vegetables

   _____   _____

   _____   _____

5. Four qualities you would like to possess

   _____   _____

   _____   _____

B. Underline each noun.

1. J. Armand Bombardier invented the snowmobile.
2. Chocolate is made from the beans of a tree that grows in the tropics.
3. The province of Québec is larger than France and Britain together.
4. The men and women rode their horses in the parade.
5. The capital of Alberta is Edmonton.
6. Alexander Graham Bell, the inventor of the telephone, was born in Edinburgh, Scotland.
7. Jack, Diane, and I took a plane to London, where we saw Buckingham Palace.
8. Many interesting animals, such as piranhas, alligators, anacondas, and sloths, live in the Amazon River Basin.
9. The tarantula is a type of large, hairy spider.
10. The Maya were a people who lived in what is now Mexico and Central America.

Common and Proper Nouns

> - There are two main types of nouns: **common nouns** and **proper nouns**.
> - A **common noun** names any one of a class of objects.
>   EXAMPLES: girl, state, author
> - A **proper noun** is the name of a particular person, place, or thing. A proper noun begins with a capital letter.
>   EXAMPLES: Wilfrid Laurier, Nova Scotia, Memorial University

A. Write a proper noun suggested by each common noun.

1. university _____
2. river _____
3. governor _____
4. singer _____
5. physician _____
6. holiday _____
7. TV show _____
8. city _____
9. teacher _____
10. classmate _____

11. car _____
12. school _____
13. lake _____
14. country _____
15. street _____
16. park _____
17. month _____
18. actor _____
19. girl _____
20. province _____

B. Write a common noun suggested by each proper noun.

1. Newfoundland _____
2. South America _____
3. Tuesday _____
4. Nile _____
5. Dr. Wilson _____
6. Lake Superior _____
7. Thanksgiving _____
8. Pacific _____
9. Arizona _____
10. David _____

11. Mars _____
12. Jean Chrétien _____
13. February _____
14. Andes Mountains _____
15. Mexico _____
16. *Treasure Island* _____
17. Jennifer _____
18. Paris _____
19. Ottawa, Ont. _____
20. Fido _____

    Unit 3, Grammar and Usage

C. Underline each common noun.

1. The sturdy <u>timber</u> of the <u>oak</u> is used in constructing <u>furniture</u>, <u>bridges</u>, and <u>ships</u>.
2. Robert Fulton was a painter, jeweller, farmer, engineer, and inventor.
3. The main crops of Puerto Rico are sugar, tobacco, coffee, and fruits.
4. The province of Nova Scotia is known as "Canada's ocean playground."
5. France has many rivers and beaches.
6. The covered bridge over the Saint John River at Hartland, New Brunswick is the longest one of its kind in the world.
7. Some of the main foods eaten in Greece are lamb, fish, olives, and feta cheese.
8. A road passes through a tunnel cut in the base of a giant tree in California.
9. Since the earliest civilizations, gold has been used for ornaments.
10. The largest lake in North America is Lake Superior.
11. The orange tree bears beautiful blossoms and delicious fruits.
12. The CN Tower in Toronto is the tallest free-standing structure in the world.
13. Pine trees give us turpentine, tar, resin, timber, and oils.
14. February always seems like the longest month of the winter.
15. The pelican, the penguin, and the flamingo are interesting birds.
16. The first trip into space was filled with danger.

D. Underline each proper noun.

1. The principal goods exported by Brazil are soybeans, sugar, and coffee.
2. Terry Fox ran all the way to Thunder Bay.
3. On the shelves of the Elm Grove Library, you will find many magical stories.
4. Commander Byrd, a naval officer, made the first airplane flight to the North Pole.
5. Dr. Singh went to McMaster University in Ontario.
6. The orange tree was brought to Europe from Asia.
7. Colombia is the world's leading producer of emeralds.
8. Kilimanjaro is the tallest mountain in Africa.
9. The Navajo make beautiful silver and turquoise jewellery.
10. Leticia and Carlos anchored the tent while Sam and Ted prepared the food.
11. During the Klondike gold rush, Dawson City was the largest city west of Winnipeg and north of Seattle.
12. Their home is on the shore of Lake Erie.
13. Québec is the only city in North America that has a wall around it.
14. Emily Carr was a writer and a painter.
15. Lemons were first grown in the valleys of India.
16. Mars is the closest planet to Earth.

Unit 3, Grammar and Usage

Lesson 23

Singular and Plural Nouns

- A **singular noun** names one person, place, or thing.
  EXAMPLES: girl, half, pear, sky
- A **plural noun** names more than one person, place, or thing.
  EXAMPLES: girls, halves, pears, skies
- Add -s to most nouns to make them plural.
  EXAMPLES: girl, girls   top, tops
- Add -es to most nouns ending in -ch, -sh, -s, or -x to make them plural.
  EXAMPLES: church, churches   brush, brushes   ax, axes
- If a noun ends in a consonant and -y, change the -y to -i and add -es.
  EXAMPLES: city, cities   army, armies
- If a noun ends in a vowel and -y, add -s to make it plural.
  EXAMPLE: boy, boys

A. Write the plural form for each noun below.

1. newspaper _____

2. guess _____

3. town _____

4. valley _____

5. body _____

6. story _____

7. bush _____

8. office _____

9. tax _____

10. toy _____

11. boss _____

12. school _____

13. day _____

14. copy _____

15. author _____

16. porch _____

B. Complete each sentence with the plural form of the noun in parentheses.

1. (penny) How many _____ make a dollar?

2. (dress) Marcy makes all of her own _____ .

3. (bridge) How many _____ were destroyed by the flood?

4. (brush) Mr. Perez got two new _____ yesterday.

5. (county) How many _____ are there in your province?

6. (fox) Seven _____ live at the zoo.

7. (book) I like to read _____ about science.

8. (lunch) She made several _____ before school.

9. (country) How many _____ are there in South America?

     Unit 3, Grammar and Usage

- Some nouns ending in -f or -fe are made plural by changing the -f or -fe to -ves.
  - EXAMPLES: loaf, loaves   wife, wives
- Some nouns ending in -f are made plural by adding -s.
  - EXAMPLES: roof, roofs   bluff, bluffs
- Most nouns ending in -o that have a vowel just before the -o are made plural by adding -s.
  - EXAMPLE: radio, radios
- Some nouns ending in -o preceded by a consonant are made plural by adding -es, but others are made plural by adding only -s.
  - EXAMPLES: potato, potatoes   piano, pianos
- A few nouns have irregular plural forms.
  - EXAMPLES: child, children   man, men   ox, oxen
- A few nouns have the same form for both the singular and plural.
  - EXAMPLES: trout, trout   sheep, sheep

C. Write the plural form for each noun below. You may wish to check the spellings in a dictionary.

1. knife _____

2. loaf _____

3. half _____

4. mouse _____

5. foot _____

6. goose _____

7. hoof _____

8. moose _____

9. life _____

10. tomato _____

11. tooth _____

12. piano _____

D. Complete each sentence with the plural form of the word in parentheses. You may wish to check the spellings in a dictionary.

1. (foot) My new shoes pinch my _____ .

2. (sheep) The shepherd always takes good care of the _____ .

3. (chimney) Many _____ were blown down during the recent storm.

4. (city) Many _____ are establishing recreation centres.

5. (leaf) The high winds scattered the dead _____ over the yard.

6. (Mosquito) _____ breed wherever there is standing water.

7. (nickel) I have five Centennial _____ .

8. (friend) He _____ arrived on the bus yesterday.

9. (desk) New _____ have been ordered for our office.

10. (bench) Concrete _____ have been placed along the walk.

Possessive Nouns

- A **possessive noun** shows possession of the noun that follows.
- Form the possessive of most singular nouns by adding an apostrophe (') and -s.
    EXAMPLES: the boy's hat   Mr. Thomas's car
- Form the possessive of a plural noun ending in -s by adding only an apostrophe.
    EXAMPLES: the Smiths' home   girls' bikes   sisters' names
- Form the possessive of a plural noun that does not end in -s by adding an apostrophe and -s.
    EXAMPLES: children's classes   men's books

A. Write the possessive form of each noun.

1. girl _____girl's_____	6. baby _____	11. brother _____
2. child _____	7. boys _____	12. soldier _____
3. women _____	8. teacher _____	13. men _____
4. children _____	9. Dr. Ray _____	14. aunt _____
5. John _____	10. ladies _____	15. Ms. Jones _____

B. Rewrite each phrase using a possessive noun.

1. the cap belonging to Jim   _____Jim's cap_____

2. the wrench that belongs to Kathy   _____

3. the smile of the baby   _____

4. the car that my friend owns   _____

5. the new shoes that belong to Kim   _____

6. the collar of the dog   _____

7. the golf clubs that Frank owns   _____

8. the shoes that belong to the runners   _____

9. the friends of our parents   _____

10. the opinion of the editor   _____

11. the lunches of the children   _____

12. the coat belonging to Kyle   _____

13. the assignment of the teacher   _____

                      Unit 3, Grammar and Usage

C. Complete each sentence with the possessive form of the word in parentheses.

1. (company) The _____ picnic will be in the park Saturday afternoon.

2. (dog) That _____ owner should pay for the damage it did.

3. (women) The _____ organization planned the meeting.

4. (Doug) _____ account of his trip was very interesting.

5. (David) _____ explanation of the problem was very clear.

6. (cat) My _____ eyes are blue.

7. (Kurt) _____ brother made the candy for our party.

8. (Men) _____ coats are sold at the store in that block.

9. (squirrel) The _____ teeth were very sharp.

10. (brother) We want to go to his _____ ranch.

11. (child) A _____ toy was found in our yard.

12. (calf) The _____ nose was soft and shiny.

13. (baby) That dog played with the _____ shoe.

14. (teachers) Her _____ names are Miss Gomez and Mr. Jacobs.

15. (Alex) We are going to _____ party tomorrow.

16. (deer) They saw a _____ tracks in the snow.

17. (Stacy) _____ work is the neatest I have ever seen.

18. (country) The _____ flag flew over the parliament buildings.

19. (robins) I have heard those _____ calls every day this week.

20. (person) That _____ speech was much too long.

21. (sister) Nichole wants to go to her _____ graduation.

22. (children) The _____ parade is held every spring.

23. (neighbours) Our _____ yards have just been mowed.

24. (class) It is this _____ time to take the test.

25. (boys) This store sells _____ clothes.

26. (designer) The _____ exhibit won first place.

27. (horse) The _____ mane is black.

Lesson 25

Appositives

- An **appositive** is a noun or phrase that identifies or explains the noun it follows.
- Use a comma before and after an appositive. If an appositive is at the end of a sentence, use a comma before it.

  EXAMPLES: Elena is graduating from Spring Hill, **her junior high school**.
  Christopher's hockey team, **the Flyers**, won every game they played.

A. Circle the appositive in each sentence. Underline the noun it identifies or explains.

1. Henry, my father's older brother, drove trains.

2. His train, a freight carrier, often had twenty cars.

3. Winnipeg, the location of the main station, was where the freight was loaded.

4. Wheat and other grains, its main cargo, were then shipped east.

5. When Henry, our uncle, came to visit, we asked many questions.

6. He never tired of telling us, his nephews, about his life.

7. Uncle Henry would joke with my father, his brother, and they laughed a great deal.

8. Uncle Henry would tease my mother, his sister-in-law, too.

9. We especially liked it when Emma, our aunt, came with him.

10. It was nice to see our cousins, Todd and Elizabeth, too.

B. Write sentences using the appositives below.

1. the cleanest room in the house   Our living room, the cleanest room in the house, is usually kept for entertaining company.

2. the most interesting subject _____

_____

3. the best day of the week _____

_____

4. my favourite sport _____

_____

5. a movie star _____

_____

6. a tropical island _____

_____

    Unit 3, Grammar and Usage

> ■ A **verb** is a word that expresses action, being, or state of being.
> EXAMPLES: Helen **went** to school. These books **are** yours.
> Elizabeth and Paul **sing** in the choir.

■ **Underline the verb in each sentence.**

1. Where are the Alps?

2. Stompin' Tom Connors wrote "Bud the Spud."

3. Check your papers carefully.

4. Bananas have great food value.

5. Africa is the home of the hippopotamus.

6. The car reached the narrow bridge.

7. Lester Pearson won a Nobel Prize.

8. Amina's father trains good mechanics.

9. Sue has a black puppy

10. How many stars are in the sky?

11. The people of our town remember the cold winter.

12. The *Bluenose* won all but one of its many races.

13. What is your favourite book?

14. They followed the old trail to the top of the hill.

15. The wind whistled around the corner.

16. Milan always watches the news.

17. Their team scored twice in the third quarter.

18. Which driver won the car race?

19. The third house from the corner is white.

20. The United States lies to the south of Canada.

21. Tom set the table for five people.

22. Answer my question.

23. Lucy explained the operation of the computer.

24. Jason worked in the flower bed for his neighbour.

25. Our town has a public swimming pool.

26. My brother plays the saxophone.

27. Brush your teeth frequently.

28. A puff of wind whirled the leaves over the lawn.

29. We arrived at our camp early in the morning.

30. Where is the launching pad?

- Some sentences contain a **verb phrase**. A verb phrase consists of a **main verb** and one or more other verbs.
  EXAMPLES: The women **are singing**. Where **have** you **been**?

■ **Underline the verb or verb phrase in each sentence.**

1. Huron warriors wore armour made of sticks.

2. Who invented the jet engine?

3. Frederick Banting was one of the discoverers of insulin.

4. The DEW line is a chain of radar stations in the North.

5. Who built the first motorcycle?

6. My friends will arrive on Saturday afternoon.

7. What was the final score?

8. Ryan has made this unusual birdhouse.

9. The waves covered the beach with many shells.

10. I have ridden on a motor scooter.

11. The artist is moulding clay.

12. Beverly and her friends spent last summer in the mountains.

13. The names of the new employees are posted by the supervisor.

14. Riswan has found a new hat.

15. She is going to the store.

16. We have trimmed the hedges.

17. Canada exports many kinds of food.

18. My friend is reading a book about World War I.

19. Adelaide Hoodless helped to educate many Canadian women.

20. Oil was discovered in many parts of Alberta.

21. Jenny Lind was called the Swedish Nightingale.

22. We are planning a car trip to Moncton, New Brunswick.

23. That dog has howled for two hours.

24. Our guests have arrived.

25. I have written letters to several companies.

26. I can name two important cities in that country.

27. The hummingbird received its name because of the sound of its wings.

28. Jan's poem was printed in the newspaper.

29. Charles and Adam are working at the hamburger stand.

30. This table was painted recently.

Helping Verbs

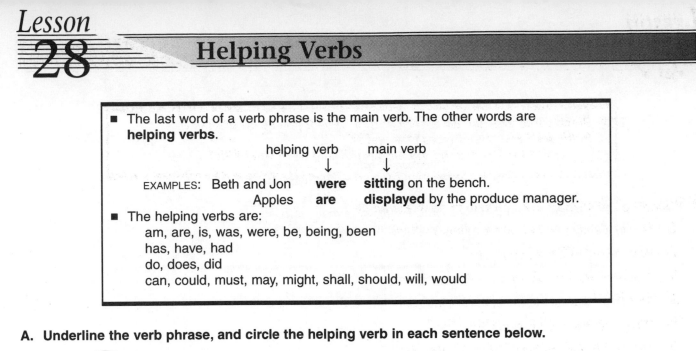

- The last word of a verb phrase is the main verb. The other words are **helping verbs**.

helping verb   main verb
     ↓   ↓

EXAMPLES: Beth and Jon **were** **sitting** on the bench.
Apples **are** **displayed** by the produce manager.

- The helping verbs are:
am, are, is, was, were, be, being, been
has, have, had
do, does, did
can, could, must, may, might, shall, should, will, would

A. Underline the verb phrase, and circle the helping verb in each sentence below.

1. We have begun our spring cleaning.

2. Molly and Zanana will rake the leaves on the front lawn.

3. Vincent and April must sweep the driveway.

4. The twins, Dawn and Daniela, will pull the weeds.

5. Christopher and his cousin, Lisa, may prepare lunch for the workers.

6. They should wash their hands first.

7. Sandwiches and fruit salad would make a delicious lunch on a hot day.

8. Our next-door neighbour is working on his lawn, too.

9. He has planted flowers in his front and back gardens.

10. Every helper must close the garbage bags tightly.

11. Squirrels, raccoons, and large crows would enjoy our garbage.

12. We might finish the outside work today.

B. Use each verb phrase in a sentence.

1. would come _____

2. should choose _____

3. had bought _____

4. might find _____

5. am writing _____

6. will learn _____

7. could become _____

8. were standing _____

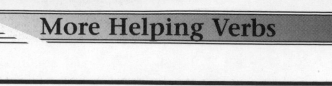

- A verb phrase may have more than one helping verb.

  helping verb   main verb
  ↓   ↓

  EXAMPLES: Bill **should have**   **taken** the bus.
  My tomato plants **have been**   **growing** very quickly.
- In a question or a sentence containing a word such as <u>not</u> or <u>never</u>, the helping verb might be separated from the main verb.
  EXAMPLES: When **will** you **decide** to fix your bicycle?
  Jason **has** not **fixed** his bicycle.

A. Underline the verb phrases, and circle the helping verbs in the sentences below.

1. Our final exam (will be) given on May 10.

2. Many students have been studying every night.

3. My friends and I may be forming a study group.

4. The study group members should be reviewing each chapter.

5. Are you joining our study group?

6. May we meet in your house one afternoon next week?

7. Kim and Naasi should have known the answers to the first ten questions.

8. Where have you been all day?

9. I have been looking everywhere for you.

10. I would have met you earlier.

11. The airplane flight has been delayed in Winnipeg.

12. Would you prefer an earlier flight?

13. No, I had been enjoying a long visit with my grandmother.

14. My parents have been waiting for over two hours in the airport.

15. Lois and Jeanine had been at the pool all day.

16. Will any other friends be swimming in the pool?

17. Several neighbourhood children must have been splashing each other.

18. Could Jessica and I take diving lessons next summer?

B. Use each verb phrase in a statement.

1. should have bought _____

2. had been finished _____

C. Use each verb phrase in a question.

1. will be going _____

2. have been practising _____

Lesson 30

Using *Is/Are* and *Was/Were*

> - Use <u>is</u> with a singular subject.
>   EXAMPLE: Tasha **is** the winner.
> - Use <u>are</u> with a plural subject.
>   EXAMPLE: The boys **are** walking home.
> - Always use <u>are</u> with the pronoun <u>you</u>.
>   EXAMPLE: You **are** absolutely right!

A. Underline the correct verb to complete each sentence.

1. (Is, Are) this tool ready to be cleaned?

2. They (is, are) making peanut brittle.

3. Bill (is, are) the chairperson this week.

4. Where (is, are) my gloves?

5. This tomato (is, are) too ripe.

6. Ryan, (is, are) these your books?

7. Daniel, (is, are) the sandwiches ready?

8. (Is, Are) you going to sing your solo this morning?

9. This newspaper (is, are) the early edition.

10. Carol asked if you (is, are) still coming to the game.

> - Use <u>was</u> with a singular subject to tell about the past.
>   EXAMPLE: I **was** there yesterday.
> - Use <u>were</u> with a plural subject to tell about the past.
>   EXAMPLE: Kevin and Ray **were** not home.
> - Always use <u>were</u> with the pronoun <u>you</u>.
>   EXAMPLE: You **were** only a few minutes late.

B. Underline the correct verb to complete each sentence.

1. Amy and Bai (was, were) disappointed because they could not go.

2. Our seats (was, were) near the stage.

3. Taro, Bill, and Oded (was, were) assigned to the first team.

4. These pencils (was, were) made by a company in Hamilton.

5. There (was, were) only one carton of milk in the refrigerator.

6. Who (was, were) that person on the corner?

7. She (was, were) at my house this morning.

8. You (was, were) the best swimmer in the contest.

9. Those tomatoes (was, were) delicious!

10. He (was, were) late for work today.

Lesson
31

Verb Tenses

> - The **tense** of a verb tells the time of the action or being.
> - **Present tense** tells that something is happening now.
>   EXAMPLES: Amanda **dances** in the show. My art lessons **start** today.
> - **Past tense** tells that something happened in the past. The action is over.
>   EXAMPLES: Amanda **danced** in the show.
>   My art lessons **started** last June.
> - **Future tense** tells that something will happen in the future. Use <u>will</u> with the verb.
>   EXAMPLES: Amanda **will dance** in the show.
>   My art lessons **will start** next month.

A. Underline the verb or verb phrase in each sentence. Then write <u>present</u>, <u>past</u>, or <u>future</u> for the tense of each verb.

1. My neighbour works four days a week. _____

2. Sometimes I care for her children, Karen and Billy. _____

3. They play in front of my house. _____

4. One day Karen threw the ball very hard to Billy. _____

5. The ball sailed over Billy's head and into the street. _____

6. Billy ran toward the street. _____

7. I shouted to Billy. _____

8. Usually, Billy listens to me. _____

9. I got the ball from the street. _____

10. Billy's mom called for him to come home. _____

11. He went as fast as possible. _____

12. Next time they will play only in the backyard. _____

B. Rewrite each sentence, changing the underlined verb to the past tense

1. My little sister <u>will follow</u> me everywhere.

    _____

2. She <u>comes</u> to my friend's house.

    _____

3. She <u>rides</u> my bicycle on the grass.

    _____

© 1997 Gage Educational Publishing Company **Unit 3, Grammar and Usage**

Principal Parts of Verbs

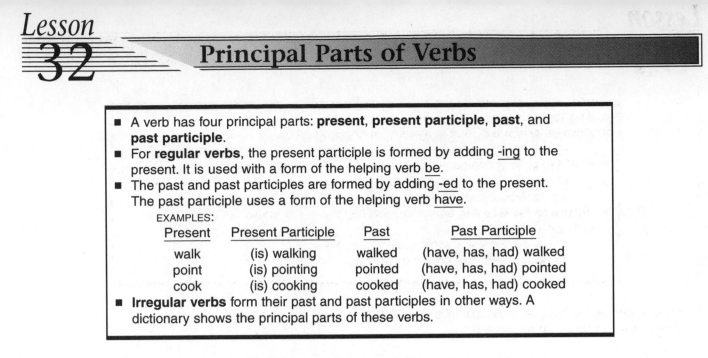

- A verb has four principal parts: **present**, **present participle**, **past**, and **past participle**.
- For **regular verbs**, the present participle is formed by adding -ing to the present. It is used with a form of the helping verb be.
- The past and past participles are formed by adding -ed to the present. The past participle uses a form of the helping verb have.

EXAMPLES:

Present	Present Participle	Past	Past Participle
walk	(is) walking	walked	(have, has, had) walked
point	(is) pointing	pointed	(have, has, had) pointed
cook	(is) cooking	cooked	(have, has, had) cooked

- **Irregular verbs** form their past and past participles in other ways. A dictionary shows the principal parts of these verbs.

■ Write the present participle, past, and past participle for each verb.

PRESENT	PRESENT PARTICIPLE	PAST	PAST PARTICIPLE
1. walk	(is) walking	walked	(have, has, had) walked
2. visit			
3. watch			
4. follow			
5. jump			
6. talk			
7. add			
8. learn			
9. paint			
10. plant			
11. work			
12. divide			
13. miss			
14. score			
15. call			
16. collect			

Lesson
33
Past Tenses of *See, Do,* and *Come*

- Never use a helping verb with: saw   did   came
- Always use a helping verb with: seen   done   come

- **Underline the correct verb form to complete each sentence.**

1. We (saw, seen) the movie.
2. Suddenly, the whole idea (came, come) to me.
3. Tammy and John (did, done) not do the ironing this morning.
4. They (saw, seen) that a lot of work had to be done to the camp.
5. Who (did, done) the framing of these prints?
6. The rain (came, come) down in sheets.
7. I haven't (did, done) all the errands for Anna.
8. I have (came, come) to help arrange the stage.
9. We have (saw, seen) many beautiful prairie flowers.
10. What have you (did, done) with the kittens?
11. My uncle (came, come) to help me move.
12. I have not (saw, seen) the new apartment today.
13. Why haven't your brothers (came, come) to help us?
14. Haven't you ever (saw, seen) a spider spinning a web?
15. When Lynne and I (came, come) in, we found a surprise.
16. I (saw, seen) the owner about the job.
17. We saw what you (did, done)!
18. Has the mail (came, come) yet?
19. The prettiest place we (saw, seen) was Cape Breton.
20. Hasn't Mohammed (did, done) a nice job of painting the room?
21. Mr. Jones (came, come) to repair the stove.
22. My dog, Max, (did, done) that trick twice.
23. Josh hadn't (came, come) to the soccer game.
24. Rebecca (saw, seen) the doctor yesterday.
25. Scott has (came, come) to the picnic.
26. Who has (saw, seen) the Rocky Mountains?
27. Deb (did, done) the decorations for the party.
28. She (came, come) to the party an hour early.
29. The bird (saw, seen) the cat near the tree.
30. The painter has (did, done) a nice job on the house.

   Unit 3, Grammar and Usage

- Never use a helping verb with: <u>ate</u>   <u>drank</u>
- Always use a helping verb with: <u>eaten</u>   <u>drunk</u>

A. Underline the correct verb form to complete each sentence.

1. Have the worms (ate, eaten) the leaves on that tree?

2. We (drank, drunk) the spring water from the mountains.

3. You (ate, eaten) more for breakfast than I did.

4. Haven't you (drank, drunk) a glass of this refreshing lemonade?

5. The hungry hikers (ate, eaten) quickly.

6. Yes, I (drank, drunk) two glasses of lemonade.

7. Have you (ate, eaten) your lunch so soon?

8. Maggie, why haven't you (drank, drunk) your tea?

9. I (ate, eaten) two delicious hamburgers for lunch.

10. We watched the birds as they (drank, drunk) from the birdbath.

11. We (ate, eaten) supper early.

12. Who (drank, drunk) a glass of tomato juice?

13. Have you ever (ate, eaten) a pink grapefruit?

14. Helma, have you (drank, drunk) an extra glass of milk?

15. Have you (ate, eaten) your breakfast yet?

16. Yes, I (drank, drunk) it about noon.

B. Write the correct past tense form of each verb in parentheses to complete each sentence.

1. (eat) Maria had _____ turkey and stuffing at Thanksgiving.

2. (drink) She _____ cranberry juice for breakfast.

3. (eat) Carlos _____ a second sandwich.

4. (drink) At the picnic we had _____ a gallon of lemonade.

5. (drink) Yes, I _____ it at about noon.

6. (eat) Cory hasn't _____ since breakfast.

7. (drink) Father _____ a glass of iced tea.

8. (eat) Did you know that those apples had been _____ ?

9. (drink) Haven't Mike and Lisa _____ the fresh orange juice?

10. (eat) The people on the train _____ in the dining car.

- Never use a helping verb with: sang   rang
- Always use a helping verb with: sung   rung

A. Underline the correct verb form to complete each sentence.

1. I have never (sang, sung) in public before.

2. Have the church bells (rang, rung)?

3. The group (sang, sung) all their songs for us.

4. The bell had not (rang, rung) at five o'clock.

5. The children (sang, sung) three folk songs.

6. We (rang, rung) their doorbell several times.

7. Which of the three sisters (sang, sung) in the talent show?

8. Who (rang, rung) the outside bell?

9. Patti, have you ever (sang, sung) for the choir director?

10. I (rang, rung) the large old bell that is beside the door.

11. Has she ever (sang, sung) this duet?

12. The church bell hasn't (rang, rung) in many years.

13. The group (sang, sung) as they had never (sang, sung) before.

14. The ship's bell hasn't (rang, rung).

15. The singer often (sang, sung) that song.

16. Have you (rang, rung) the bell on that post?

B. Write the correct past tense form of the verb in parentheses to complete each sentence.

1. (ring)   It was so noisy that we couldn't tell if the bell had _____ .

2. (sing)   Maria _____ a solo.

3. (sing)   She had never _____ alone before.

4. (ring)   The bells _____ to announce their marriage yesterday.

5. (ring)   Have you _____ the bell yet?

6. (sing)   Who _____ the first song?

7. (ring)   The group _____ bells to play a tune.

8. (sing)   Hasn't she _____ before royalty?

9. (ring)   The boxer jumped up as the bell _____ .

10. (sing)   That young boy _____ a solo.

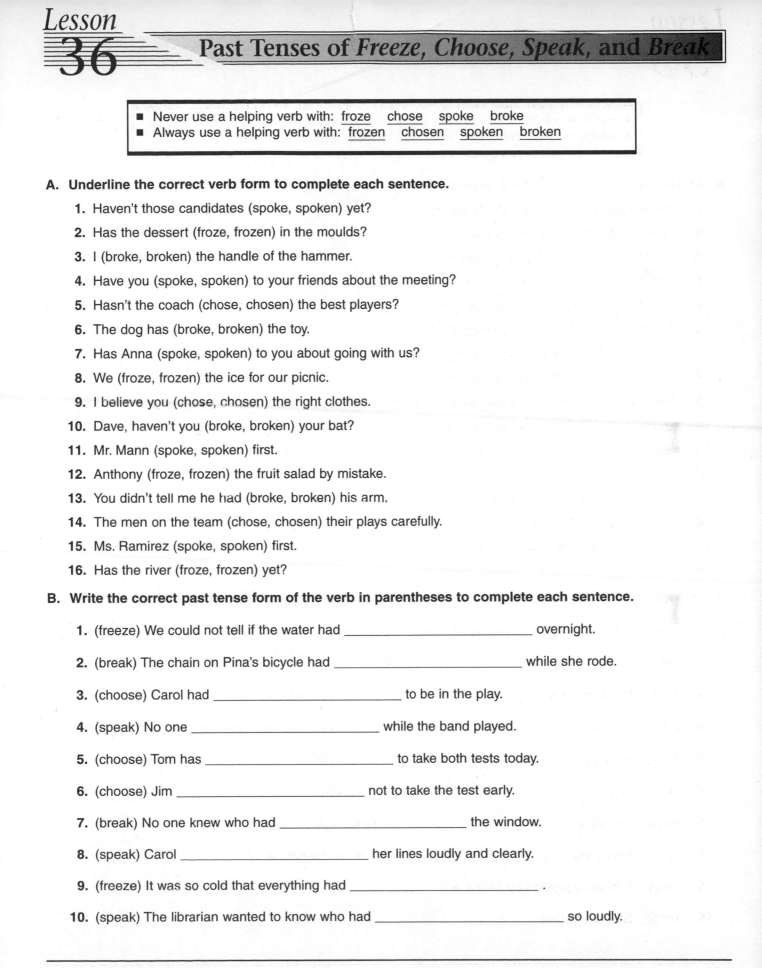

Lesson 36

Past Tenses of *Freeze, Choose, Speak,* and *Break*

- Never use a helping verb with: <u>froze</u>   <u>chose</u>   <u>spoke</u>   <u>broke</u>
- Always use a helping verb with: <u>frozen</u>   <u>chosen</u>   <u>spoken</u>   <u>broken</u>

A. Underline the correct verb form to complete each sentence.

1. Haven't those candidates (spoke, spoken) yet?

2. Has the dessert (froze, frozen) in the moulds?

3. I (broke, broken) the handle of the hammer.

4. Have you (spoke, spoken) to your friends about the meeting?

5. Hasn't the coach (chose, chosen) the best players?

6. The dog has (broke, broken) the toy.

7. Has Anna (spoke, spoken) to you about going with us?

8. We (froze, frozen) the ice for our picnic.

9. I believe you (chose, chosen) the right clothes.

10. Dave, haven't you (broke, broken) your bat?

11. Mr. Mann (spoke, spoken) first.

12. Anthony (froze, frozen) the fruit salad by mistake.

13. You didn't tell me he had (broke, broken) his arm.

14. The men on the team (chose, chosen) their plays carefully.

15. Ms. Ramirez (spoke, spoken) first.

16. Has the river (froze, frozen) yet?

B. Write the correct past tense form of the verb in parentheses to complete each sentence.

1. (freeze) We could not tell if the water had _____ overnight.

2. (break) The chain on Pina's bicycle had _____ while she rode.

3. (choose) Carol had _____ to be in the play.

4. (speak) No one _____ while the band played.

5. (choose) Tom has _____ to take both tests today.

6. (choose) Jim _____ not to take the test early.

7. (break) No one knew who had _____ the window.

8. (speak) Carol _____ her lines loudly and clearly.

9. (freeze) It was so cold that everything had _____ .

10. (speak) The librarian wanted to know who had _____ so loudly.

Unit 3, Grammar and Usage   © 1997 Gage Educational Publishing Company   **47**

> - Never use a helping verb with: <u>knew</u>   <u>grew</u>   <u>threw</u>
> - Always use a helping verb with: <u>known</u>   <u>grown</u>   <u>thrown</u>

A. Underline the correct verb form to complete each sentence.

1. We have (knew, known) her family for years.

2. Weeds (grew, grown) along the park paths.

3. Hasn't Julia (threw, thrown) the softball?

4. I have never (knew, known) a more courageous person.

5. Katie's plants have (grew, grown) very rapidly.

6. How many times have you (threw, thrown) at the target?

7. Has Jonathan (grew, grown) any unusual plants this year?

8. I (knew, known) every person at the meeting.

9. I wish that my hair hadn't (grew, grown) so much this year.

10. Brian, how long have you (knew, known) Lee?

11. The pitcher has (threw, thrown) three strikes in a row.

12. I don't know why the plants (grew, grown) so fast.

13. We (threw, thrown) out many old boxes.

14. Mr. Low has (grew, grown) vegetables this summer.

15. Marty (knew, known) the correct answer.

16. The guard (threw, thrown) the ball to the centre.

17. She is the nicest person I have ever (knew, known).

18. The sun (grew, grown) brighter in the afternoon.

B. Write one original sentence with <u>knew</u>. Then write one sentence with <u>known</u>.

1. _____

2. _____

C. Write one original sentence with <u>grew</u>. Then write one sentence with <u>grown</u>.

1. _____

2. _____

D. Write one original sentence with <u>threw</u>. Then write one sentence with <u>thrown</u>.

1. _____

2. _____

                    Unit 3, Grammar and Usage

- Never use a helping verb with: <u>blew</u>   <u>flew</u>
- Always use a helping verb with: <u>blown</u>   <u>flown</u>

A. Underline the correct verb form to complete each sentence.

1. Flags (flew, flown) from many houses on Canada Day.

2. The train whistles have (blew, blown) at every crossing.

3. The birds haven't (flew, flown) south for the winter.

4. The wind (blew, blown) the kites to pieces.

5. The candles (blew, blown) out too soon.

6. Has your friend (flew, flown) her new kite?

7. Yes, she (flew, flown) it this morning.

8. All the papers have (blew, blown) across the floor.

9. Four people (flew, flown) their model airplanes in the tournament.

10. The wind has (blew, blown) like this for an hour.

11. I didn't know that you had (flew, flown) here in a jet.

12. Hasn't the train whistle (blew, blown) yet?

13. The airplanes (flew, flown) in an aviation show.

14. Our largest maple tree had (blew, blown) down last night.

15. The striped hot-air balloon has (flew, flown) the farthest.

16. The judge (blew, blown) the whistle as the runner crossed the finish line.

17. The Carsons have (flew, flown) to Europe.

18. An erupting volcano (blew, blown) the mountain apart.

19. The geese (flew, flown) in formation.

20. The curtains have (blew, blown) open from the breeze.

21. The movie star (flew, flown) in a private jet.

22. A tornado (blew, blown) the roof off a house.

23. A pair of ducks has (flew, flown) overhead.

B. Write one original sentence with <u>blew</u>. Then write one sentence with <u>blown</u>.

1. _____

2. _____

C. Write one original sentence with <u>flew</u>. Then write one sentence with <u>flown</u>.

1. _____

2. _____

- Never use a helping verb with: took   wrote
- Always use a helping verb with: taken   written

A. Underline the correct verb form to complete each sentence.

1.   They (took, taken) the first plane to Calgary.

2.   Who has (wrote, written) the best script for the play?

3.   Mike hadn't (took, taken) these pictures last summer.

4.   Who (wrote, written) the minutes of our last meeting?

5.   We (took, taken) down our paintings.

6.   Farley Mowat has (wrote, written) many stories about animals.

7.   I (took, taken) my watch to the jeweller for repair.

8.   I (wrote, written) for a video catalogue.

9.   Haven't you (took, taken) your medicine yet?

10. Diana, have you (wrote, written) to your friend?

11. Tran (took, taken) too much time getting ready.

12. Mei hadn't (wrote, written) these exercises with a pen.

13. Who (took, taken) my magazine?

14. Mario (wrote, written) an excellent business letter.

B. Write the correct past tense form of the verb in parentheses to complete each sentence.

1.   (write)   Who _____ this short theme?

2.   (take)   It has _____ me a long time to make this planter.

3.   (write)   Jean Little had _____ this poem.

4.   (take)   The children have _____ off their muddy shoes.

5.   (write)   We _____ letters to our member of parliament.

6.   (take)   Louisa, have you _____ your dog for a walk?

7.   (write)   My cousin _____ me a letter about his new house.

8.   (write)   Dorothy Livesay _____ David's favourite poem.

9.   (take)   Willie and Sharon _____ the bus to the park.

10. (write)   Mr. Bustos _____ an excellent article for our newspaper.

11. (take)   The nurse _____ my temperature.

- Never use a helping verb with: <u>gave</u>   <u>went</u>
- Always use a helping verb with: <u>given</u>   <u>gone</u>

A. Underline the correct verb form to complete each sentence.

1. Ms. Morris has (gave, given) that land to the city.

2. Where has Anu (went, gone) this afternoon?

3. Vladimir (gave, given) a speech on collecting rare coins.

4. My friends (went, gone) to the park an hour ago.

5. Mary, who (gave, given) you this ruby ring?

6. Rob and Carter have (went, gone) to paint the house.

7. Mr. Edwards (gave, given) us ten minutes to take the test.

8. Elaine has (went, gone) to help Eileen find the place.

9. My friends (gave, given) clothing to the people whose house burned.

10. Hasn't Jan (went, gone) to the store yet?

11. The sportscaster has just (gave, given) the latest baseball scores.

12. Charlie (went, gone) to apply for the job.

13. Have you (gave, given) Fluffy her food?

14. Has Miss Martinson (went, gone) to Springfield?

15. I have (gave, given) my horn to my cousin.

16. Paula has (went, gone) to sleep already.

B. Write the correct past tense form of the verb in parentheses to complete each sentence.

1. (go) Paula _____ to sleep already.

2. (give) Has Mrs. Tate _____ the cheques to the other employees?

3. (go) Every person had _____ before you arrived.

4. (give) My neighbour was _____ a ticket for speeding.

5. (go) Haven't the Yamadas _____ to Japan for a month?

6. (give) Ms. O'Malley has _____ me a notebook.

7. (go) Haven't you ever _____ to an aquarium?

8. (give) I _____ her my new address.

9. (go) Michael _____ to camp for a week.

10. (give) Ms. Rosen has _____ me driving lessons.

- A **possessive pronoun** is a pronoun that shows ownership of something.
- The possessive pronouns <u>hers</u>, <u>mine</u>, <u>ours</u>, <u>theirs</u>, and <u>yours</u> stand alone.
    - EXAMPLES: The coat is **mine**. The shoes are **yours**.
- The possessive pronouns <u>her</u>, <u>its</u>, <u>my</u>, <u>our</u>, <u>their</u>, and <u>your</u> must be used before nouns.
    - EXAMPLES: **Her** car is red. **Our** car is black.
- The pronoun <u>his</u> may be used either way.
    - EXAMPLES: That is **his** dog. The dog is **his**.

- **Underline the possessive pronoun in each sentence.**

1. Lora lost her bracelet.

2. David broke his arm.

3. The dogs wagged their tails.

4. The referee blew her whistle.

5. The students should take their books.

6. Oscar Peterson is famous for his piano playing.

7. Brad entered his sculpture in the contest.

8. I wanted to read that book, but a number of its pages are missing.

9. My aunt and uncle have sold their cottage.

10. The Inuit built igloos out of snow blocks.

11. How did Canada get its name?

12. Daniel showed the group his wonderful stamp collection.

13. Coffee found its way from Arabia to Java.

14. The magpie builds its nest very carefully.

15. Pam sprained her ankle while skiing.

16. Lisa drove her car to the top of the peak.

17. Frank left his raincoat in the doctor's office.

18. Isn't B.C. noted for its salmon?

19. Travis brought his mother a beautiful shawl from India.

20. Gina, where is your brother?

21. Manuel forgot about his appointment with the dentist.

22. Joel and Andrew have gone to their swimming lesson.

23. Sandra showed her report to the boss.

24. Juan gave his father a beautiful paperweight.

25. Mr. Owens found his keys.

26. The children broke their swing.

Lesson 42

Indefinite Pronouns

> - An **indefinite pronoun** is a pronoun that does not refer to a specific person or thing.
>   > EXAMPLES: **Someone** is coming to speak to the group.
>   > Does **anyone** know what time it is?
>   > **Everybody** is looking forward to the trip.
> - Some indefinite pronouns are negative.
>   > EXAMPLES: **Nobody** has a ticket.
>   > **No one** was waiting at the bus stop.
> - The indefinite pronouns <u>anybody</u>, <u>anyone</u>, <u>anything</u>, <u>each</u>, <u>everyone</u>, <u>everybody</u>, <u>everything</u>, <u>nobody</u>, <u>no one</u>, <u>nothing</u>, <u>somebody</u>, <u>someone</u>, and <u>something</u> are singular. They take singular verbs.
>   > EXAMPLE: **Everyone is** ready.
> - The indefinite pronouns <u>both</u>, <u>few</u>, <u>many</u>, <u>several</u>, and <u>some</u> are plural. They take plural verbs.
>   > EXAMPLE: **Several** of us **are** ready.

A. Underline the Indefinite pronoun in each sentence below.

1. Everyone helped complete the project.
2. Is somebody waiting for you?
3. Anything is possible.
4. Something arrived in the mail.
5. Everybody looked tired at practice.
6. No one was willing to work longer.
7. Does anyone have a dollar?
8. Both of us were tired.
9. Nothing was dry yet.
10. Does anybody want to go swimming?
11. Someone should speak up.
12. Everybody is hungry now.
13. Each of the cats was black.
14. Some of the dogs bark all the time.
15. Several were empty.
16. No one remembered to bring it.
17. Everyone started to feel nervous.
18. Nobody admitted to being afraid.
19. Everything will be explained.
20. Is anything missing?

B. Complete each sentence with an indefinite pronoun.

1. I can't believe that _____ in my desk has disappeared.

2. Is _____ coming to teach you to run the computer?

3. Every person in class attended today. _____ was absent.

4. She tried to call, but _____ answered the phone.

5. Does _____ remember the address?

6. There is _____ here to see you.

7. Would _____ like a piece of cake?

8. The party was so much fun. _____ enjoyed it.

Lesson
43

Subject Pronouns

> - A **subject pronoun** is used as the subject or as part of the subject of a sentence
> - The subject pronouns are I, you, he, she, it, we, and they.
>   EXAMPLE: **It** has beautiful wings.
> - When the pronoun I is used with nouns or other pronouns, it is always named last.
>   EXAMPLE: Marie and **I** caught a butterfly.

- **Underline the correct pronoun.**

1. Carolyn and (I, me) helped repair the car.
2. (She, Her) is going to the studio.
3. Why can't Leigh and (I, me) go with them?
4. (She, Her) and Charles skated all afternoon.
5. Jaclyn and (I, me) are going to Belgium tomorrow.
6. (He, Him) played tennis this morning.
7. Beth and (he, him) were five minutes late yesterday morning.
8. (She, Her) and (I, me) spent an hour in the library.
9. Joanne and (I, me) worked until nine o'clock.
10. (He, Him) and Yuri are going over there now.
11. May (we, us) carry your packages?
12. (They, Them) and I are buying some groceries.
13. Sarah and (I, me) are going with her to the park.
14. (It, Them) wagged its tail.
15. (She, You) have a beautiful singing voice, Claire.
16. (He, Him) is the owner of the suitcase.
17. Crystal and (I, me) are on the same team.
18. (She, Her) has started a book club.
19. (We, Us) are planning a bike trip.
20. (They, Them) are going to see a Shakespearean play.
21. Is (she, her) your favourite singer?
22. Martin and (I, me) would be happy to help you.
23. (We, Us) work at the post office.
24. Juan and (we, us) are painting the front porch.
25. (He, Him) excels as a photographer.
26. (She, Her) has known us for several years.
27. (I, Me) am the director of the community choir.

■ An **object pronoun** is used after an action verb or a preposition, such as <u>after</u>, <u>against</u>, <u>at</u>, <u>between</u>, <u>except</u>, <u>for</u>, <u>from</u>, <u>in</u>, <u>of</u>, <u>to</u>, and <u>with</u>.

■ The object pronouns are <u>me</u>, <u>you</u>, <u>him</u>, <u>her</u>, <u>it</u>, <u>us</u>, and <u>them</u>.
   EXAMPLE: The gift was for **him**.

■ When the pronoun <u>me</u> is used with nouns or other pronouns, it is always last.
   EXAMPLE: The books were for Kay and **me**.

■ **Underline the correct pronoun.**

1. Tony, are you going with Stephanie and (I, me) to see Rosa?

2. Scott invited Patrick and (I, me) to a movie.

3. I am going to see Mary and (she, her) about this problem.

4. The woman told (us, we) to come for her old magazines.

5. I went with Jan and (she, her) to the hobby show.

6. That dinner was prepared by (them, they).

7. Ajay asked Andrew and (I, me) to the soccer game.

8. Emily and Bev congratulated (he, him).

9. Sharon praised (him, he) for his work.

10. Will you talk to (she, her) about the trip?

11. Ben, can you go with Renee and (I, me)?

12. Pam lectured (us, we) about being on time.

13. The package was leaning against (it, we).

14. They brought the problem to (we, us).

15. It was too hard for (they, them) to solve.

16. Richard gave (I, me) his old goalie's equipment.

17. Anthony is teaching (we, us) Morse code.

18. Please inform (he, him) of the change of plans.

19. Brian offered to help (I, me) hang the curtains.

20. That car belongs to (he, him).

21. Carl didn't see (they, them).

22. Nancy asked him to take a picture of (we, us).

23. Please wait for (she, her) after school.

24. She is in the class with (he, him).

25. Hand the packages to (they, them).

26. Was this really discovered by (she, her)?

27. Would you like to go to dinner with (we, us)?

Lesson
45
Subject Pronouns after Linking Verbs

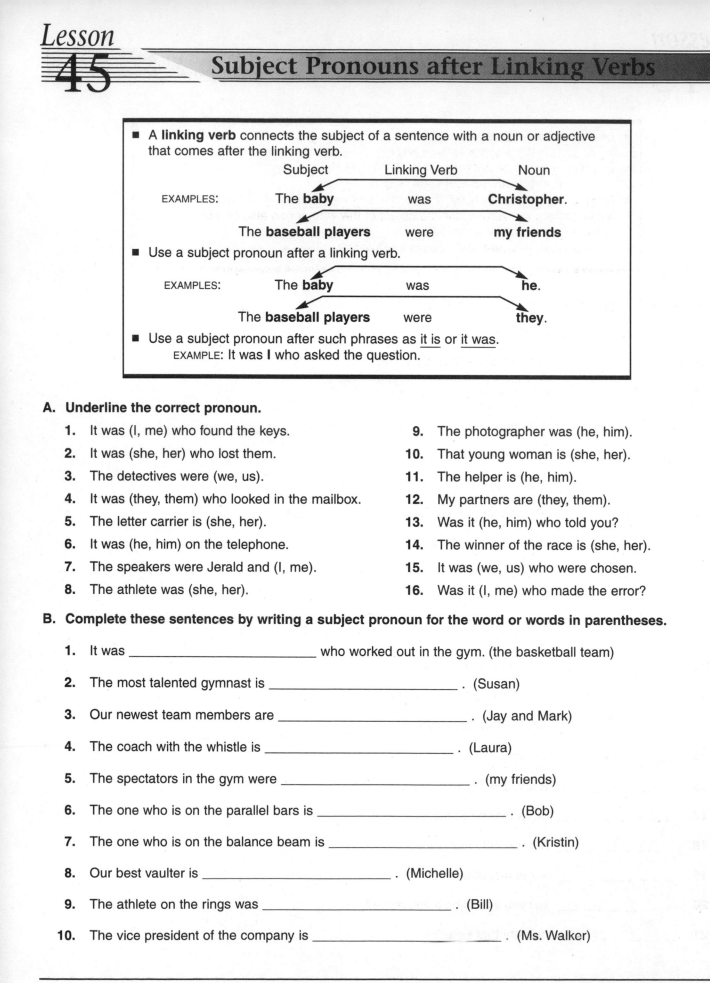

- A **linking verb** connects the subject of a sentence with a noun or adjective that comes after the linking verb.

	Subject	Linking Verb	Noun
EXAMPLES:	The **baby**	was	**Christopher**.
	The **baseball players**	were	**my friends**

- Use a subject pronoun after a linking verb.

EXAMPLES:	The **baby**	was	**he**.
	The **baseball players**	were	**they**.

- Use a subject pronoun after such phrases as <u>it is</u> or <u>it was</u>.
  EXAMPLE: It was **I** who asked the question.

A. Underline the correct pronoun.

1. It was (I, me) who found the keys.
2. It was (she, her) who lost them.
3. The detectives were (we, us).
4. It was (they, them) who looked in the mailbox.
5. The letter carrier is (she, her).
6. It was (he, him) on the telephone.
7. The speakers were Jerald and (I, me).
8. The athlete was (she, her).

9. The photographer was (he, him).
10. That young woman is (she, her).
11. The helper is (he, him).
12. My partners are (they, them).
13. Was it (he, him) who told you?
14. The winner of the race is (she, her).
15. It was (we, us) who were chosen.
16. Was it (I, me) who made the error?

B. Complete these sentences by writing a subject pronoun for the word or words in parentheses.

1. It was _____ who worked out in the gym. (the basketball team)

2. The most talented gymnast is _____ . (Susan)

3. Our newest team members are _____ . (Jay and Mark)

4. The coach with the whistle is _____ . (Laura)

5. The spectators in the gym were _____ . (my friends)

6. The one who is on the parallel bars is _____ . (Bob)

7. The one who is on the balance beam is _____ . (Kristin)

8. Our best vaulter is _____ . (Michelle)

9. The athlete on the rings was _____ . (Bill)

10. The vice president of the company is _____ . (Ms. Walker)

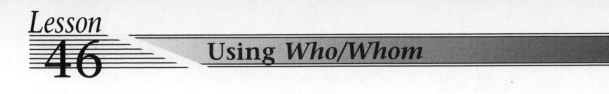

> - Use <u>who</u> as a subject pronoun.
>   EXAMPLE: **Who** came to the party?
> - Use <u>whom</u> as an object pronoun.
>   EXAMPLE: **Whom** did the nurse help?
> - By rearranging the sentence <u>The nurse did help **whom?**</u>, you can see that <u>whom</u> follows the verb and is the object of the verb. It can also be the object of a preposition.
>   EXAMPLE: To **whom** did you wish to speak?

- **Complete each sentence with <u>Who</u> or <u>Whom</u>.**

1. _____Who_____ is that man?

2. _____ made the first moon landing?

3. _____ would you choose as the winner?

4. _____ is your best friend?

5. _____ gets the reward?

6. _____ will be staying with you this summer?

7. _____ did the instructor invite to speak to the class?

8. _____ did you see at the park?

9. _____ will you contact at headquarters?

10. _____ will you write about?

11. _____ is available to baby-sit for me on Saturday?

12. _____ did you drive to the store?

13. _____ would like to travel to Cuba next summer?

14. _____ raced in the track meet?

15. _____ did they meet at the airport?

16. _____ are your three favourite authors?

17. _____ owns that new blue car?

18. _____ did you help last week?

19. _____ wrote that clever poem?

20. _____ will you ask to help you move?

21. _____ brought that salad?

Using Pronouns

■ Underline the pronouns in each sentence below.

1. He went with us to the picnic by the lake.

2. Did you find a magazine in the living room?

3. When are we going to meet at the concert?

4. Are we leaving today?

5. Did you see him?

6. She saw them at the party.

7. He spoke to James and me.

8. Who brought the music for you to play?

9. Yvonne and I invited them to go to a movie.

10. Mary brought me these pictures she took.

11. Why can't they go with us?

12. I went with her to get the application form.

13. Louis brought you and him some French coins.

14. Between you and me, I think that last program was silly.

15. Did Dorothy explain the experiment to her and him?

16. Did she find them?

17. May I go with you?

18. He and I sat on the benches.

19. They saw me this morning.

20. Who has a library book?

21. For whom shall I ask?

22. I do not have it with me.

23. She told me about the trip to Germany.

24. They are coming to see us.

25. We haven't heard from James since he left.

26. Come with us.

27. Aren't you and I going with Alan?

28. You should plan the theme before you write it.

29. Aren't they coming for us?

30. Sachiko and I gave them a new book of stamps.

31. Steve told us an interesting story about a dog.

32. Who is planning a summer vacation?

33. She and I never expected to see you here!

34. We will visit them this evening.

Lesson 48

More Pronouns

■ **Underline the correct pronoun.**

1. It was (I, me).

2. Bill and (he, him) are on their way to catch the plane.

3. Nicole and (I, me) have always been good friends.

4. The guard showed (they, them) the entrance to the building.

5. The boss told (I, me) to clean the office.

6. Please take (I, me) to lunch.

7. I am going to wait for (she, her).

8. (Who, Whom) planted those beautiful flowers?

9. Next Saturday Boris and (I, me) are going fishing.

10. Marie came to see (us, we).

11. To (who, whom) did you send the postcard?

12. This is a secret between you and (I, me).

13. Kevin asked Carolyn to move (us, our) table.

14. The committee asked Michael, Kip, and (I, me) to help serve.

15. Did Ellen bring (she, her)?

16. Jamie told (us, we) to get to the station on time.

17. Grant and (she, her) drove the tractors.

18. (Who, Whom) bought this magazine?

19. The boss brought Matt and Kevin (them, their) cheque.

20. Martin took Armando and (I, me) to work this morning.

21. With (who, whom) did you play soccer?

22. Michelle painted (she, her) kitchen yesterday.

23. Seven of (us, we) were named to the board of directors.

24. He completed all of (his, him) math problems this morning.

25. (Us, We) are going to play basketball.

26. She called for Olga and (I, me).

27. (Who, Whom) washed the windows?

28. Joyce and (I, me) will fix the broken latch.

29. We came to see (them, they).

30. Will Pamela or (I, me) go with Jason to (him, his) cabin?

31. For (who, whom) are you looking?

32. Did you know it was (her, she)?

33. Lisa and (her, she) are painting the chairs.

34. (We, Us) are going to the museum on Saturday.

> ■ An **adjective** is a word that describes a noun or a pronoun.
>   EXAMPLE: The sky is spotted with **white** clouds.
> ■ Adjectives usually tell **what kind**, **which one**, or **how many**.
>   EXAMPLES: **white** roses, **that** mitt, **fifteen** cents

A. Choose an appropriate adjective from the box to describe each noun.

brave	foolish	gorgeous	hasty	shiny
cold	fragrant	happy	polite	sly

1. _____ scout
2. _____ flower
3. _____ worker
4. _____ water
5. _____ fox

6. _____ girls
7. _____ sunset
8. _____ dimes
9. _____ prank
10. _____ deeds

B. Write three adjectives that could be used to describe each noun.

1. flowers   _____ _____ _____

2. an automobile   _____ _____ _____

3. a friend   _____ _____ _____

4. a bicycle   _____ _____ _____

5. snow   _____ _____ _____

6. a baby   _____ _____ _____

7. a sunrise   _____ _____ _____

8. a book   _____ _____ _____

9. a kitten   _____ _____ _____

10. a train   _____ _____ _____

11. a mountain   _____ _____ _____

12. the wind   _____ _____ _____

13. a river   _____ _____ _____

14. a house   _____ _____ _____

- The **articles** <u>a</u>, <u>an</u>, and <u>the</u> are called **limiting adjectives**.
- Use <u>a</u> before words beginning with a consonant sound.
    - EXAMPLES: **a** bugle, **a** mountain, **a** sail
- Use <u>an</u> before words beginning with a vowel sound.
    - EXAMPLES: **an** oboe, **an** island, **an** anchor

C. Write <u>a</u> or <u>an</u> in each blank.

1. _____ salesperson
2. _____ train
3. _____ newspaper
4. _____ iceberg
5. _____ friend
6. _____ election
7. _____ welder
8. _____ piano
9. _____ game
10. _____ ant
11. _____ eye
12. _____ army
13. _____ telephone
14. _____ orange
15. _____ country
16. _____ airplane
17. _____ oak
18. _____ engine
19. _____ ear
20. _____ province
21. _____ elm
22. _____ shoe
23. _____ object
24. _____ basket
25. _____ apple

26. _____ ounce
27. _____ error
28. _____ tablet
29. _____ desk
30. _____ holiday
31. _____ accident
32. _____ astronaut
33. _____ box
34. _____ fire
35. _____ pilot
36. _____ mechanic
37. _____ entrance
38. _____ evergreen
39. _____ aviator
40. _____ hundred
41. _____ picture
42. _____ elephant
43. _____ letter
44. _____ umbrella
45. _____ announcer
46. _____ onion
47. _____ umpire
48. _____ car
49. _____ ice cube
50. _____ elevator

Lesson 50

Proper Adjectives

■ A **proper adjective** is an adjective that is formed from a proper noun. It always begins with a capital letter.

	EXAMPLES:	**Proper Noun**	**Proper Adjective**
		Poland	Polish
		Germany	German
		Paris	Parisian

A. Write a proper adjective formed from each proper noun below. You may wish to check the spelling in a dictionary.

1. South America _____
2. Africa _____
3. England _____
4. Mexico _____
5. France _____
6. Russia _____
7. America _____
8. Rome _____
9. Alaska _____

10. Canada _____
11. Norway _____
12. Scotland _____
13. Ireland _____
14. China _____
15. Spain _____
16. Italy _____
17. Hawaii _____
18. Japan _____

B. Write sentences using proper adjectives you formed in Exercise A.

1. Many South American countries have warm climates. _____

2. _____

3. _____

4. _____

5. _____

6. _____

7. _____

8. _____

9. _____

10. _____

- A **demonstrative adjective** is an adjective that points out a specific person or thing.
- This and that describe singular nouns. This points to a person or thing nearby, and that points to a person or thing farther away.
  - EXAMPLES: **This** room is my favourite. **That** man is running very fast.
- These and those describe plural nouns. These points to persons or things nearby, and those points to persons or things farther away.
  - EXAMPLES: **These** women are the best players. **Those** houses need painting.
- The word them is a pronoun. Never use it to describe a noun.

A. Underline the correct demonstrative adjective.

1. Please hand me (those, this) red candles.

2. Where did you buy (these, that) large pecans?

3. Did you grow (these, them) roses in your garden?

4. Please bring me (those, that) wrench.

5. Where did Marc find (these, this) watermelon?

6. (Those, Them) glasses belong to Mike.

7. Do you want one of (these, this) calendars?

8. May I use one of (these, them) pencils?

9. Did you see (those, them) films of Africa?

10. Calvin, where are (those, that) people going?

11. Did you see (those, them) police officers?

12. Please put (those, this) books in the box.

13. (That, Those) floor needs to be cleaned.

14. Sarah and Joe might buy (those, that) car.

15. (That, These) cabinets will be repainted.

16. Please close (that, those) door.

17. Will you fix the flat tire on (this, these) bike?

18. (This, Those) letter needs a stamp before you mail it.

B. Write four sentences using this, that, these, or those.

1. _____

2. _____

3. _____

4. _____

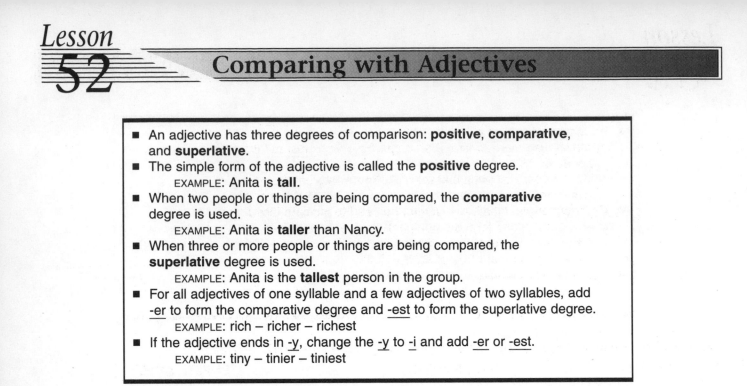

- An adjective has three degrees of comparison: **positive**, **comparative**, and **superlative**.
- The simple form of the adjective is called the **positive** degree.
      EXAMPLE: Anita is **tall**.
- When two people or things are being compared, the **comparative** degree is used.
      EXAMPLE: Anita is **taller** than Nancy.
- When three or more people or things are being compared, the **superlative** degree is used.
      EXAMPLE: Anita is the **tallest** person in the group.
- For all adjectives of one syllable and a few adjectives of two syllables, add -er to form the comparative degree and -est to form the superlative degree.
      EXAMPLE: rich – richer – richest
- If the adjective ends in -y, change the -y to -i and add -er or -est.
      EXAMPLE: tiny – tinier – tiniest

■ **Write the comparative and superlative forms.**

POSITIVE	COMPARATIVE	SUPERLATIVE
1. smooth	_____	_____
2. young	_____	_____
3. sweet	_____	_____
4. strong	_____	_____
5. lazy	_____	_____
6. great	_____	_____
7. kind	_____	_____
8. calm	_____	_____
9. rough	_____	_____
10. narrow	_____	_____
11. deep	_____	_____
12. short	_____	_____
13. happy	_____	_____
14. cold	_____	_____
15. pretty	_____	_____

■ For some adjectives of two syllables and all adjectives of three or more syllables, use <u>more</u> to form the comparative and <u>most</u> to form the superlative.

    EXAMPLES: He thinks that the lily is **more** fragrant than the tulip.

    He thinks that the carnation is the **most** fragrant flower of all.

■ Comparison of adjectives also can be used to indicate less or least of a quality. Use <u>less</u> to form the comparative and <u>least</u> to form the superlative.

    EXAMPLES: I see Jo **less** often than I see Terry.

    I see Josh **least** often of all.

■ Some adjectives have irregular comparisons.

    EXAMPLES: good, better, best   bad, worse, worst

A. Write the comparative and superlative forms using <u>more</u> and <u>most</u>.

POSITIVE	COMPARATIVE	SUPERLATIVE
1. energetic		
2. courteous		
3. impatient		
4. important		
5. difficult		
6. wonderful		
7. gracious		
8. agreeable		

B. Write the comparative and superlative forms using <u>less</u> and <u>least</u>.

POSITIVE	COMPARATIVE	SUPERLATIVE
1. helpful		
2. friendly		
3. serious		
4. agreeable		
5. faithful		
6. comfortable		
7. patient		
8. reliable		

C. Write the correct degree of comparison for the adjective in parentheses.

1. (near)   Which planet is _____ the earth, Venus or Jupiter?

2. (tall)   Who is the _____ of the three people?

3. (helpful)   Who is _____ , Pota or Linda?

4. (young)   Who is _____ , Jack or Tim?

5. (difficult)   I think this is the _____ problem in the lesson.

6. (good)   Is "A Ghost Story" a _____ story than "The Last Leaf"?

7. (small)   What is our _____ province?

8. (hot)   In our region, August is usually the _____ month.

9. (young)   Hans is the _____ person at the factory.

10. (wide)   The Amazon is the _____ river in the world.

11. (old)   Who is _____ , David or Steve?

12. (large)   What is the _____ city in your province?

13. (courteous)   Dan is always the _____ person at a party.

14. (good)   This poem is the _____ one I have read this year.

15. (cold)   This must be the _____ night so far this winter.

16. (studious)   Of the two sisters, Andrea is the _____ .

17. (tall)   Who is _____ , Kay or Carol?

18. (wealthy)   This is the home of the _____ banker in our city.

19. (fast)   Who is the _____ worker in the office?

20. (useful)   Which is _____ , electric lights or the telephone?

21. (beautiful)   Your garden is the _____ one I have seen.

22. (narrow)   That is the _____ of all the bridges on the road.

23. (large)   Calgary is _____ than Edmonton.

24. (good)   Of the three books, this one is the _____ .

25. (bad)   That is the _____ collection in the museum.

26. (large)   Sudbury has the _____ nickel in the world.

27. (beautiful)   I think tulips are the _____ kind of flower.

Adverbs

- An **adverb** is a word that describes a verb, an adjective, or another adverb.
  EXAMPLES: The parade moved **slowly**. Your tie is **very** colourful.
  You did this **too** quickly
- An adverb usually tells **how**, **when**, **where**, or **how often**.
- Many adverbs end in -<u>ly</u>.

A. Write two adverbs that could be used to describe each verb.

1. laugh _____

2. talk _____

3. stand _____

4. sing _____

5. swim _____

6. eat _____

7. read _____

8. work _____

9. write _____

10. walk _____

11. jump _____

12. move _____

13. run _____

14. speak _____

15. listen _____

16. drive _____

17. sit _____

18. dance _____

B. Use each adverb in a sentence.

well	regularly	early
softly	very	here

1. _____

2. _____

3. _____

4. _____

5. _____

6. _____

C. Underline the adverb or adverbs in each sentence.

1. The old car moved slowly up the hill.

2. She answered him very quickly.

3. We arrived at the party too early, so we helped with the decorations.

4. The family waited patiently to hear about the newborn baby.

5. Cindy drove the car very cautiously in the snowstorm.

6. Does Marshall always sit here, or may I have this seat?

7. They walked very rapidly in order to get home before the rainstorm.

8. The dog ran swiftly toward its home.

9. Emily quietly waited her turn while others went ahead.

10. These oaks grow very slowly, but they are worth the long wait.

11. May I speak now, or should I wait for his call?

12. We searched everywhere for the inflatable rafts and life preservers.

13. The nights have been extremely warm, so we go swimming every evening.

14. He always speaks distinctly and practises good manners.

15. Can you swim far underwater without coming up for air?

16. Come here, and I'll show you ladybugs in the grass.

17. Please answer quickly so that we can finish before five o'clock.

18. Deer run very fast, especially at the first sign of danger.

19. I suddenly remembered that I left my jacket in the park.

20. The snow fell softly on the rooftops of the mountain village.

21. I can pack our lunches and be there by noon.

22. She wrote too rapidly and made a mistake.

23. Winters there are extremely cold, but summers are very pleasant.

24. The pianist bowed politely to the audience.

25. You are reading too rapidly to learn something from it.

26. The team played extremely well.

27. The cat walked softly toward a fly on the windowpane.

28. Everyone listened carefully to the sound of a bluebird singing.

29. We walked wearily toward the bus in the hot sun.

30. We crossed the street very carefully at the beginning of the parade.

31. We eagerly watched the game from the rooftop deck of our building.

32. The recreation centre was finished recently.

33. We walked everywhere yesterday.

34. My friend dearly loves her red hat.

35. I have read this book before.

36. He wants badly to learn to play the guitar.

 Unit 3, Grammar and Usage

- An **adverb** has three degrees of comparison: **positive**, **comparative**, and **superlative**.
- The simple form of the adverb is called the **positive** degree.
    EXAMPLE: Joe worked **hard** to complete the job.
- When two actions are being compared, the **comparative** degree is used.
    EXAMPLE: Joe worked **harder** than Jim.
- When three or more actions are being compared, the **superlative** degree is used.
    EXAMPLE: Tony worked **hardest** of all.
- Use -er to form the comparative degree and use -est to form the superlative degree of one-syllable adverbs.
- Use more or most with longer adverbs and with adverbs that end in -ly.
    EXAMPLE: Jan danced **more** gracefully than Tania.
    Vicki danced the **most** gracefully of all.

- **Complete each sentence using the comparative or superlative form of the underlined adverb.**

1. David can jump <u>high</u>. Diane can jump _____ than David.

    Donna can jump the _____ of all.

2. Grant arrives <u>late</u> for the party. Gina arrives _____

    than Grant. Gail arrives the _____ of anyone.

3. Dawn walks <u>slowly</u> in the park. Tomas walks _____

    than Dawn. Sam walks _____ of all.

4. Jean spoke <u>clearly</u> before the class. Jon spoke _____

    than Jean. Joseph spoke _____ of all the students.

5. Alex scrubbed <u>hard</u>. Anne scrubbed _____ than Alex.

    Alice scrubbed the _____ of all.

6. You can can get to the store <u>quickly</u> on foot. If you take your bicycle you will

    arrive there _____ .

    A car will get you to your destination _____ of all.

7. Tania played the flute <u>beautifully</u>. Tara played the clarinet even _____ .

    Rick played the oboe the _____ of them all.

8. Ahmed has been waiting <u>long</u>. Mr. Norris has been waiting even _____ .

    Justin has been waiting the _____ of all.

> - Doesn't is the contraction of <u>does not</u>. Use it with singular nouns and the pronouns <u>he</u>, <u>she</u>, and <u>it</u>.
>   - EXAMPLES: The dog **doesn't** want to play. She **doesn't** want to go.
> - Don't is the contraction of <u>do not</u>. Use it with plural nouns and the pronouns <u>I</u>, <u>you</u>, <u>we</u>, and <u>they</u>.
>   - EXAMPLES: The children **don't** have their books. We **don't** have time.

■ **Underline the correct contraction to complete each sentence.**

1. I (doesn't, don't) know why he (doesn't, don't) like that movie star.

2. Why (doesn't, don't) the caretaker open the gates earlier?

3. (Doesn't, Don't) your sister coach the team, Tom?

4. (Doesn't, Don't) this office need more fresh air?

5. (Doesn't, Don't) this sweater belong to you, Katie?

6. We (doesn't, don't) go home at noon for lunch.

7. (Doesn't, Don't) your friend attend Queen's University?

8. Terry (doesn't, don't) want to miss the parade.

9. Angelo (doesn't, don't) like to play tennis.

10. It (doesn't, don't) take long to learn to swim.

11. Some of the elevators (doesn't, don't) go to the top floor.

12. Eric (doesn't, don't) know how to drive a car.

13. He (doesn't, don't) know that we are here.

14. We (doesn't, don't) listen to our radio often.

15. Why (doesn't, don't) Craig get here on time?

16. This problem (doesn't, don't) seem difficult to me.

17. (Doesn't, Don't) it look hot outside?

18. Why (doesn't, don't) Paul go, too?

19. She (doesn't, don't) want to go to the movie.

20. Kelly (doesn't, don't) have that written in her notebook.

21. (Doesn't, Don't) you want to go with us?

22. Why (doesn't, don't) your friend come to our meetings?

23. Neil (doesn't, don't) go to night school.

24. Yin (doesn't, don't) eat ice cream.

25. Jody and Ray (doesn't, don't) like science fiction movies.

26. The people (doesn't, don't) have to wait outside.

27. (Doesn't, Don't) you want to come with us?

28. They (doesn't, don't) know if it will rain today.

       Unit 3, Grammar and Usage

- Use <u>may</u> to ask for permission.
  - EXAMPLE: **May** I go with you?
- Use <u>can</u> to express the ability to do something.
  - EXAMPLE: James **can** swim well.

A. Complete each sentence with <u>may</u> or <u>can</u>.

1. Adam, _____ you whistle?

2. His dog _____ do three difficult tricks.

3. Miss Nance, _____ I leave work early?

4. I _____ see the airplane in the distance.

5. Chris, _____ you tie a good knot?

6. Cargos, _____ I drive your car?

7. You _____ see the mountains from here.

8. My friend _____ drive us home.

9. The Garcias _____ speak three languages.

10. _____ I examine those new books?

- Teach means "to give instruction."
  - EXAMPLE: I'll **teach** you how to shoot free throws.
- Learn means "to acquire knowledge."
  - EXAMPLE: When did you **learn** to speak Spanish?

B. Complete each sentence with <u>teach</u> or <u>learn</u>.

1. I think he will _____ me quickly.

2. I will _____ to recite that poem.

3. Did Jamie _____ you to build a fire?

4. The women are going to _____ to use the new machines.

5. Will you _____ me to play tennis?

6. My brother is going to _____ Billy to skate.

7. Would you like to _____ the rules of the game to them?

8. No one can _____ you if you do not try to _____ .

- ■ <u>Sit</u> means "to take a resting position." Its principal parts are <u>sit</u>, <u>sitting</u>, and <u>sat</u>.
  EXAMPLES: Please **sit** here. He **sat** beside her.
- ■ <u>Set</u> means "to place." Its principal parts are <u>set</u>, <u>setting</u>, and <u>set</u>.
  EXAMPLES: Will you please **set** this dish on the table?
  She **set** the table for dinner last night.

A. Underline the correct verb.

1. Please (sit, set) down, Kathleen.

2. Where should we (sit, set) the television?

3. Where do you (sit, set)?

4. Pamela, please (sit, set) those plants out this afternoon.

5. (Sit, Set) the basket of groceries on the patio.

6. Chico usually (sits, sets) on this side of the table.

7. Please come and (sit, set) your books down on that desk.

8. Have you ever (sat, set) by this window?

9. Does he (sit, set) in this seat?

10. Why don't you (sit, set) over here?

- ■ <u>Lie</u> means "to recline" or "to occupy a certain space." Its principal parts are <u>lie</u>, <u>lying</u>, <u>lay</u>, and <u>lain</u>.
  EXAMPLES: Why don't you **lie** down for a while?
  He **has lain** in the hammock all afternoon.
- ■ <u>Lay</u> means "to place." Its principal parts are <u>lay</u>, <u>laying</u>, and <u>laid</u>.
  EXAMPLES: The workers **are laying** new carpeting in the house.
  Who **laid** the wet towel on the table?

B. Underline the correct verb.

1. Where did you (lie, lay) your gloves, Beth?

2. (Lie, Lay) down, Spot.

3. He always (lies, lays) down to rest when he is very tired.

4. Where have you (lain, laid) the evening paper?

5. Please (lie, lay) this box on the desk.

6. Do not (lie, lay) on that dusty floor.

7. (Lay, Lie) the papers on top of the desk.

8. I (laid, lain) the shovel on that pile of dirt.

9. I need to (lie, lay) down to rest.

10. She has (laid, lain) on the sofa all morning.

Lesson 59

Prepositions

> - A **preposition** is a word that shows the relationship of a noun or a pronoun to another word in the sentence.
>   EXAMPLES: Put the package **on** the table.
>   Place the package **in** the desk.
> - These are some commonly used prepositions:
>
> | about | against | at | between | from | of | through | under |
> | above | among | behind | by | in | on | to | upon |
> | across | around | beside | for | into | over | toward | with |

- **Draw a line under each preposition in the sentences below.**

1. The grin on Juan's face was bright and warm.

2. He greeted his cousin from Brazil with a smile and a handshake.

3. They walked through the airport and toward the baggage area.

4. Juan found his bags between two boxes.

5. The two cousins had not seen each other for five years.

6. They could spend hours talking about everything.

7. Juan and Luis got into Juan's truck.

8. Juan drove Luis to Juan's family's farm.

9. It was a long ride across many hills and fields.

10. Luis rested his head against the seat.

11. Soon they drove over a hill and into a valley.

12. The farm was located across the Bow River.

13. The house stood among a group of oak trees.

14. Juan parked the truck beside the driveway.

15. They walked across the driveway and toward the house.

16. Juan's mother, Anita, stood behind the screen door.

17. Juan's family gathered around Luis.

18. Everyone sat on the porch and drank lemonade.

19. "Tell us about our relatives in Brazil," Rosa asked.

20. "You have over twenty cousins in my area," said Luis.

21. They go to school, just like you do.

22. Then everyone went into the house and ate dinner.

23. Juan's family passed the food across the table.

24. "Many of these dishes come from old family recipes," he said.

25. "It is wonderful to be among so many relatives," Luis said.

26. After dinner, everyone went to the living room.

27. Luis showed them photographs of his home in Brazil.

■ A **prepositional phrase** is a group of words that begins with a preposition and ends with a noun or pronoun.

>   EXAMPLE: Count the **books on the shelf**.

■ The noun or pronoun in a prepositional phrase is called the **object of the preposition**.

>   EXAMPLE: Count the books on the **shelf**.

■ **Put parentheses around each prepositional phrase. Then underline each preposition, and circle the object of the preposition.**

1. The fathers (of Confederation) had a vision (of a great country).

2. We climbed into the station wagon.

3. Many stars can be seen on a clear night.

4. The top of my desk has been varnished.

5. Have you ever gone through a tunnel?

6. Place these memos on the bulletin board.

7. We have a display of posters in the showcase in the corridor.

8. Yolanda, take these reports to Ms. Kaniganti.

9. What is the capital of Turkey?

10. The fabric on this antique sofa came from France.

11. Are you a collector of minerals?

12. I am going to Julia's house.

13. The hillside was dotted with beautiful wild flowers.

14. The rain beat against the windowpanes.

15. We placed a horseshoe above the door.

16. This poem was written by my oldest sister.

17. Great clusters of grapes hung from the vine.

18. Is he going to the race?

19. A herd of goats grazed on the hillside.

20. Are you carrying those books to the storeroom?

21. Our car stalled on the bridge.

22. My family lives in St. Sauveur.

23. A small vase of flowers was placed in the centre of the table.

24. The group sat around the fireplace.

25. The cold wind blew from the north.

26. Doris hit the ball over the fence.

27. The dog played with the bone.

28. High weeds grow by the narrow path.

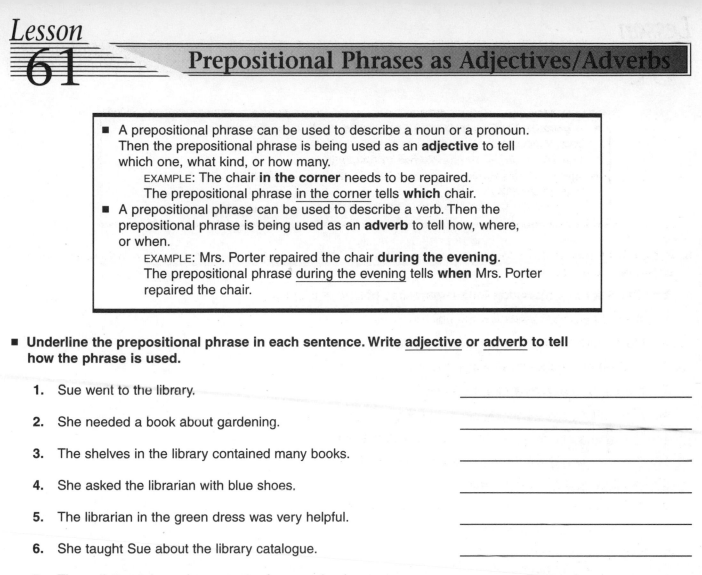

- A prepositional phrase can be used to describe a noun or a pronoun. Then the prepositional phrase is being used as an **adjective** to tell which one, what kind, or how many.
  - EXAMPLE: The chair **in the corner** needs to be repaired.
  - The prepositional phrase <u>in the corner</u> tells **which** chair.
- A prepositional phrase can be used to describe a verb. Then the prepositional phrase is being used as an **adverb** to tell how, where, or when.
  - EXAMPLE: Mrs. Porter repaired the chair **during the evening**.
  - The prepositional phrase <u>during the evening</u> tells **when** Mrs. Porter repaired the chair.

- **Underline the prepositional phrase in each sentence. Write <u>adjective</u> or <u>adverb</u> to tell how the phrase is used.**

1. Sue went to the library. _____

2. She needed a book about gardening. _____

3. The shelves in the library contained many books. _____

4. She asked the librarian with blue shoes. _____

5. The librarian in the green dress was very helpful. _____

6. She taught Sue about the library catalogue. _____

7. The online catalogue has an entry for every book. _____

8. The books are organized by call number. _____

9. Some gardening books were in the health section. _____

10. Sue's trip to the library was a great success. _____

11. She took several books with her. _____

12. Sue read them at home. _____

13. The window seat in the living room was her favourite spot. _____

14. Sue looked out the window. _____

15. Her own garden by the backyard fence was dead. _____

16. The vegetables from last year's garden had been delicious. _____

17. She would plant more vegetables near the house. _____

18. Then she would have many vegetables in the summer. _____

- A **conjunction** is a word used to join words or groups of words.
    EXAMPLES: Sally **and** Barb worked late. We worked **until** he arrived.
- These are some commonly used conjunctions:

although	because	however	or	that	until	whether
and	but	if	since	though	when	while
as	for	nor	than	unless	whereas	as yet

- Some conjunctions are used in pairs. These include <u>either . . . or,</u> <u>neither . . . nor</u>, and <u>not only . . . but also</u>.

A. Underline each conjunction in the sentences below.

1. We waited until the mechanic replaced the part.

2. Plums and peaches are my favourite fruits.

3. The wind blew, and the rain fell.

4. Please call Alan or Grant for me.

5. A conjunction may connect words or groups of words.

6. Cotton and wheat are grown on nearby farms.

7. Neither Ann nor Bonnie is my cousin.

8. Their home is not large, but it is comfortable.

9. Ron and Atiya arrived on time.

10. Do not move the vase, for you may drop it.

B. Complete each sentence with a conjunction.

1. I cannot leave _____ the baby-sitter arrives.

2. We must hurry, _____ we'll be late for work.

3. Battles were fought on the sea, on the land, _____ in the air.

4. Charle _____ Rick went to the movie, _____ Donald did not.

5. Please wait _____ Elizabeth gets ready.

6. Fong _____ I will carry that box upstairs.

7. Peter _____ Dan are twins.

8. We will stay home _____ you cannot go.

9. This nation exports lumber _____ wheat.

10. _____ the children _____ the parents liked the violent movie.

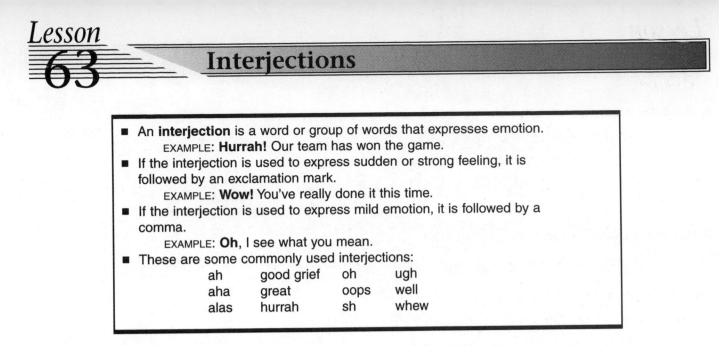

- An **interjection** is a word or group of words that expresses emotion.
  - EXAMPLE: **Hurrah!** Our team has won the game.
- If the interjection is used to express sudden or strong feeling, it is followed by an exclamation mark.
  - EXAMPLE: **Wow!** You've really done it this time.
- If the interjection is used to express mild emotion, it is followed by a comma.
  - EXAMPLE: **Oh**, I see what you mean.
- These are some commonly used interjections:

ah	good grief	oh	ugh
aha	great	oops	well
alas	hurrah	sh	whew

■ **Write sentences with the following interjections.**

1. Ah _____

2. Wow _____

3. Oh _____

4. Ugh _____

5. Ouch _____

6. Oops _____

7. Hurrah _____

8. Oh no _____

9. Hey _____

10. Sh _____

11. Help _____

12. Well _____

13. Whew _____

14. Oh my _____

15. Hush _____

16. Hooray _____

17. Aha _____

18. Ha _____

A. Underline each common noun. Circle each proper noun.

1. John Morgan is the president of companies in Calgary, Alberta, and London, England.

2. Dr. Margaret Howe is a professor of business and economics at Simon Fraser University.

3. Friends and relatives visiting our cabin on Lake Erie can enjoy swimming, fishing, boating, and hiking.

B. Write the plural form for each noun below.

_____ **1.** magazine

_____ **2.** flash

_____ **3.** pony

_____ **4.** potato

_____ **5.** elf

_____ **6.** stereo

C. Complete each sentence with the possessive form of the word in parentheses.

1. (parents) The _____ group held a book sale at the school.

2. (children) The _____ classes came at different times.

3. (teachers) All of the _____ favourite books were there.

4. (singers) The _____ voices blended perfectly together.

D. Underline the correct verb or the correct pronoun.

1. Have you (saw, seen) Matthew this morning?

2. Vince (did, done) all of the driving.

3. Marta (came, come) home a few minutes ago.

4. I (took, taken) my bicycle to the shop last Saturday.

5. Where has your friend (went, gone)?

6. I haven't (wrote, written) my invitations yet.

7. Gina (gave, given) her report yesterday.

8. It (don't, doesn't) take much time to walk to the store.

9. Where (was, were) you going yesterday?

10. Mark will go with Pam and (I, me) to visit Angela.

11. Bella and (I, me) signed up for music lessons.

12. Please take (we, us) with you when you go to the mall.

13. (They, Them) wanted to watch the Olympic Games on television.

14. (He, Him) was worried about finishing the test on time.

15. Give (they, them) those books and boxes.

     Unit 3, Grammar and Usage

E. Underline the correct pronouns in each sentence.

1. Mark will go with Pam and (I, me) to visit (us, our) friend Maria.
2. Beth and (I, me) will take singing lessons from (she, her).
3. Our friends will let (we, us) ride with (they, them).
4. (We, Us) will watch the Olympic Games at (their, they) house.
5. (He, Him) was worried that (her, she) would get lost.
6. (Who, Whom) is that woman with (he, him)?
7. It was (me, I) who found (him, his) dog.
8. She told the answer to (whom, who)?

F. Underline each adjective. Circle each adverb.

1. This short coat fit comfortably last year.
2. The large basket was filled with pink roses.
3. Many mistakes are caused by carelessness.
4. The fastest runners ran easily to the finish line.
5. She carefully followed the complicated directions of the new recipe.

G. Circle the correct form of each adjective or adverb.

1. Sven is the (youngest, younger) person to ever win a medal.
2. The neighbour's new dog barks (louder, loudest) than our dog.
3. The last singer in the talent show sang the (more beautifully, most beautifully) of all.
4. Jim swims (fastest, faster) than Paul.
5. She is (taller, tallest) than her brothers.

H. Underline the correct word in parentheses that completes each sentence.

1. Please (lie, lay) the books on the table.
2. I (don't, doesn't) understand your request.
3. You must (learn, teach) how to listen better.
4. Maybe you (may, can) tell me again.
5. Please (set, sit) down, and we'll talk.
6. I'd rather be (lying, laying) down.
7. It (don't, doesn't) matter what you are doing.
8. I will (learn, teach) you something you don't know.

I. Put parentheses around each prepositional phrase. Then underline each preposition and circle the object of the preposition.

1. Put this basket of clothes in the laundry room.
2. The hillside was covered with yellow daisies.
3. The top of the mountain is usually covered with snow.
4. The house on the corner was sold in one week.

Using What You've Learned

A. Read the following paragraphs.

Christopher Columbus was born in the city of Genoa, Italy, around 1451. His father, a weaver, made cloth. Columbus learned many sailing skills because he grew up close to the sea. He worked on an Italian merchant ship and was shipwrecked on the rocky coast of Portugal. While he was in Portugal, he quickly learned new ways to build ships and to navigate. Columbus made several voyages along the African coast and even travelled as far north as Iceland

Columbus first suggested the idea of sailing west to find a route to Japan and China to King John II of Portugal. The king was not interested, so Columbus went to the rulers of Spain, King Ferdinand and Queen Isabella. In 1492, the king and queen wisely granted their permission to Columbus and gave him three ships: the *Niña*, the *Pinta*, and the *Santa Maria*. Columbus set sail with a crew of ninety men.

B. In the paragraphs, find six common nouns, and write them on the lines below. Circle those that are plural.

1. _____   3. _____   5. _____

2. _____   4. _____   6. _____

C. Find six proper nouns, and write them on the lines below.

1. _____   3. _____   5. _____

2. _____   4. _____   6. _____

D. Find two proper adjectives and the nouns they describe, and write them on the lines below.

1. _____   2. _____

E. Find two adverbs and the verbs they describe, and write them on the lines below.

1. _____   2. _____

F. Find a sentence with an appositive, and write the sentence on the lines below.

_____

_____

G. Find six prepositional phrases, and write them on the lines below.

1. _____   4. _____

2. _____   5. _____

3. _____   6. _____

   Unit 3, Grammar and Usage

H. Rewrite the following paragraph. Correct any mistakes in the use of nouns, pronouns, or verbs.

Nobody knows if ghost's really exists, but some strange story has been reported. In the early days, settlers believed that, because North America was youngest than Europe, it could not have any ghosts. One of the more famous ghost stories ever took place in Sydney, Nova Scotia. Two soldier's said they seen the figure of a very pale young man walking past they. The figures white face looks at them sadly before disappearing. One of the soldiers thought it look like his brother, whom he thought were alive and well back in England. He finds out later that this brother have died at the exact moment the ghostly figure appeared!

Using Capital Letters

> ■ **Capitalize** the first word of a sentence.
> > EXAMPLE: Let's take a walk to the park.
> ■ Capitalize the first word of a quotation.
> > EXAMPLE: Joseph said, "It's time for lunch."

A. Circle each letter that should be capitalized. Write the capital letter above it.

1. haven't you made an appointment to meet them?

2. the teenagers will go to the game together.

3. danielle asked, "how did she like the book?"

4. the family moved to another province last year.

5. "bring your scripts to the practice," said the director.

6. who wrote this article for the newspaper?

7. the woman said, "my party is in one week."

8. "have some more carrot sticks," said the host.

> ■ Capitalize the first word of every line of poetry.
> > EXAMPLE: The strong winds whipped
> > The sails of the ship
> ■ Capitalize the first, last, and all important words in the titles of books, poems, songs, and stories.
> > EXAMPLES: *Who Has Seen the Wind*   "Happy Birthday to You"

B. Circle each letter that should be capitalized. Write the capital letter above it.

1. i eat my peas with honey;

   i've done it all my life.

   it makes the peas taste funny,

   but it keeps them on the knife!

2. it's midnight, and the setting sun

   is slowly rising in the west;

   the rapid rivers slowly run,

   the frog is on his downy nest.

3. Who wrote the poem "torontosaurus rex"?

4. My favourite novel is *a wrinkle in time*.

5. The high school band played "stand by me."

6. During the summer, Kim read *anne of avonlea*.

7. Carla gave her poem the title "chasing the wind."

> - Capitalize all **proper nouns**.
>   EXAMPLES: Sarah, Dad, Arbour Street, England, Halifax, Arctic Ocean,
>   Ural Mountains, Valentine's Day, February, Academy School, *Ocean Queen*
> - Capitalize all **proper adjectives**. A proper adjective is an adjective that is
>   made from a proper noun.
>   EXAMPLES: the Spanish language, American food, Chinese people

C. Rewrite the following paragraph. Be sure to add capital letters where they are needed.

Chris and her friends went to a festival in winnipeg, manitoba. Some of them tasted greek pastry and Canadian cheese soup. charlie thought that the italian sausage and mexican tacos were delicious! laurel tried an unusual japanese salad. They all watched some irish folk dancers and listened to german music.

_____

_____

_____

_____

_____

_____

_____

_____

D. Circle each letter that should be capitalized. Write the capital letter above it.

1. Did anita and her family drive through b.c., alberta, and saskatchewan?

2. Isn't brazil larger in area than the united states?

3. Did emily carr live in the small city of victoria, british columbia?

4. Have you read the story of laura secord?

5. I have been reading about the solomon islands.

6. The north sea is connected with the english channel by the strait of dover.

7. At thirteen, thalia and her family moved to québec from canso, n.s.

8. Isn't montréal the oldest city in canada?

9. Is nairobi the capital of kenya?

10. Our friend brought japanese money back from her trip.

> ■ Capitalize a person's title when it comes before a name.
>   EXAMPLES: Judge Schmidt, Reverend Wilson
> ■ Capitalize abbreviations of titles.
>   EXAMPLES: Dr. Wong, Supt. Barbara Shurna, Mr. J. Howell, Sr.

E. Circle each letter that should be capitalized. Write the capital letter above it.

1. Did captain cheng congratulate sergeant walters on his promotion?

2. The new health plan was developed by dr. ruth banks and mr. yuri stein.

3. After an introduction, pres. alice slater presented the next speaker, mr. allen norman.

4. When did principal grissom invite mayor hadley to attend the graduation ceremony?

5. Officer halpern was the first to stand up when judge patterson entered the courtroom.

6. How long has mrs. frank been working for president howell?

7. Does prof. magda schneider teach this course, or does dr. david towne?

8. Prince andrew of england will tour the country in the fall.

9. Senator alan howell is the uncle of supt. joyce randall.

> ■ Capitalize abbreviations of days and months, parts of addresses, and titles of members of the armed forces. Also capitalize all letters in postal codes and in abbreviations for provinces.
>   EXAMPLES: Fri., Jan., 3720 Huron Ave. E., Gen. H. J. Farrimond, Goose Bay, NF, Duck Lake, MB

F. Circle each letter that should be capitalized. Write the capital letter above it.

1. capt. margaret k. hansen
   2075 lakeview st.
   gimli, mb r0c 1b3

2. jackson school Track Meet
   at Wilson stadium
   tues., sept. 26, 10:30
   649 clark blvd. n,

3. mr. jonathan bernt
   150 telson rd.
   scarborough, ontario m3p 4a2

4. lt. gary l. louis
   5931 progress rd.
   glace bay, ns b1a 5e9

5. thanksgiving Concert
   wed., oct. 9, 11:00
   Practice tues., oct. 8, 3:30
   See ms. evans for details.

6. gen. david grimes
   329 hayes st. n.
   louisville, ky 40227

Using End Punctuation

> ■ Use a **period** at the end of a declarative sentence.
>   EXAMPLE: Theresa's aunt lives in Saskatchewan.
> ■ Use a **question mark** at the end of an interrogative sentence.
>   EXAMPLE: Will you carry this package for me?

A. Use a period or question mark to end each sentence below.

1.   Ms. Clark has moved her law office ___

2.   Isn't this Dorothy's baseball glove ___

3.   Are you moving to Markham next month ___

4.   It's too late to buy tickets for the game ___

5.   Our program will begin in five minutes ___

6.   Does your sister drive a truck ___

7.   Ms. Tobin's store was damaged by the flood ___

8.   Are you going to Rebecca's party ___

9.   Lucy did not take the plane to Moncton ___

10. Do you have a stamp for this envelope ___

11. Have you ever seen Mahdi laugh so hard ___

12. President Sophia Harris called the meeting to order ___

13. Will Gilmore Plumbing be open on Labour Day ___

14. School ends the second week in June ___

15. We are going camping in British Columbia this summer ___

B. Add the correct end punctuation where needed in the paragraph below.

Have you ever been to the Olympic Games ___ If not, have you ever seen them on television ___ I hope to see them in person some day ___ The Olympic Games are held every four years in a different country ___ The games started in ancient Greece, but the games as we now know them date back to 1896 ___ Some of the finest athletes in the world compete for bronze, silver, and gold medals ___ Can you think of a famous Olympic athlete ___ What is your favourite Olympic sport ___ It could be a winter or summer sport because the games are held for each season ___ Donovan Bailey won a gold medal in the 100-metre sprint ___ Can you imagine how excited that athlete must have felt, knowing that he had represented Canada so well ___ He holds the world record to date ___ However, there will be plenty more chances for that record to be broken ___

- Use a period at the end of an imperative sentence.
  EXAMPLE: Close the door to the attic.
- Use an **exclamation point** at the end of an exclamatory sentence and after an interjection that shows strong feelings.
  EXAMPLES: What a great shot! I'd love to go with you! Wow!

C. Add periods and exclamation points where needed in the sentences below.

1. Address the envelope to Dr. George K. Zimmerman _____

2. How nicely dressed you are _____

3. Hurry _____ The bus is ready to leave _____

4. Get some paints for your next art lesson _____

5. Shake hands with Mr. D. B. Norton _____

6. Oops _____ I spilled the glass of orange juice _____

7. Carry this bag to the car in the parking lot _____

8. What a great view you have from your apartment window _____

9. Wipe the counter when you're through eating _____

10. Oh, what a beautiful painting _____

11. I can't wait until the summer holidays _____

12. Please take this to the post office for me _____

13. Just look at the size of the fish he caught _____

14. I've never seen a larger one _____

15. Get the net from under the life preserver _____

16. I hope the pictures come out well _____

D. Add the correct end punctuation where needed in the paragraph below.

There are a lot of strange creatures in the insect world ___ Have you ever heard of ice worms ___ Some live in glaciers in the Canadian North ___ Ice worms are usually black ___ They feed on the algae that grows around the glaciers ___ What an odd sight they must be ___ Another type of ice worm is found in the Canadian Rockies ___ Do you know how long its egg takes to hatch ___ It takes a whole year ___ The larva lives for another five years ___ The adult worm only lives about two years ___ Ice worms cannot survive at temperatures above 7 degrees Celsius or below -7 degrees Celsius ___ The Inuit have a legend about a woolly worm ___ It is called Sikusi ___ Sikusi frees people who get trapped in the ice ___ Of course, the real ice worms are only four centimetres long ___ That is hardly long enough to be much help ___

 Unit 4, Capitalization and Punctuation

Using Commas

> ■ Use a **comma** between words or groups of words in a series.
> EXAMPLE: Be sure your business letter is brief, courteous, and correct.
> ■ Use a comma before a conjunction in a compound sentence.
> EXAMPLE: Neal sketched the cartoon, and Clare wrote the caption.

A. Add commas where needed in the sentences below.

1. Canada exports wheat lumber and other natural resources.

2. The children played softball ran races and pitched horseshoes.

3. Lauren held the nail and Tasha hit it with a hammer.

4. Alice Henry Carmen and James go to the library often.

5. The pitcher threw a fastball and the batter struck out.

6. Sara peeled the peaches and Victor sliced them.

7. The mountains were covered with forests of pine cedar and oak.

8. Craig should stop running or he will be out of breath.

9. Baseball is Lee's favourite sport but Sue's favourite is hockey.

10. You can swim camp or sail in Collingwood and Owen Sound.

11. The rain fell steadily and the lightning flashed.

12. Mindy enjoyed the corn but Frank preferred the string beans.

> ■ Use a comma to set off a quotation from the rest of a sentence.
> EXAMPLES: "We must get up early," said Mom.
> Mom said, "We must get up early."

B. Add commas before or after the quotations below.

1. "Please show me how this machine works" said Raisa.

2. "Be sure you keep your eyes on the road" said the driving instructor.

3. Rick replied "I can't believe my ears."

4. Gail said "Travel is dangerous on the icy roads."

5. "Paul studied piano for two years" said Ms. Walters.

6. Alex said "That goat eats everything in sight."

7. "Let's go to the park for a picnic" said Marie.

8. "Wait for me here" said Paul.

9. Tom said "Sandra, thank you for the present."

10. "I'm going to the game with Al" remarked Frank.

11. Al asked "What time should we leave?"

12. Chris remembered "I was only five when we moved to Toronto."

> ■ Use a comma to set off the name of a person who is being addressed.
>   EXAMPLE: Betty, did you find the answer to your question?
> ■ Use a comma to set off words like yes, no, well, and oh at the beginning
>   of a sentence.
>   EXAMPLE: No, I haven't seen Jack today.
> ■ Use a comma to set off an appositive.
>   EXAMPLE: Jack, Mary's brother, is going to university next fall.

C. Add commas where needed in the sentences below.

1. Miss Hunt do you know the answer to that question?

2. Can't you find the book I brought you last week Roger?

3. Dr. Levin the Smith's dentist sees patients on weekends.

4. Oh I guess it takes about an hour to get to Calgary.

5. Joe may Sam and I go to the ball game?

6. Our neighbour Billy Johnson is a carpenter.

7. What is the population of your city Linda?

8. Well I'm not sure of the exact number.

9. Soula are you going skiing this weekend?

10. What time are you going to the concert Greg?

11. Joseph our friend coaches the lacrosse team.

12. Sue have you seen a small black cat around your neighbourhood?

13. Pierre do you know Mr. D. B. Norton?

14. No I don't think we've ever met.

15. Sally and John would you like to go shopping on Saturday?

16. Mrs. Porter the principal is retiring this year.

17. Yes the teachers are planning a retirement dinner for her.

18. Mrs. Porter and her husband Hal plan to move to New Brunswick.

D. Add commas where needed in the paragraph below.

I have two friends who are always there for me and I tell them everything. So it was a surprise to me when Carol my oldest friend said "Well when are you moving?" I said "What do you mean?" She said "I don't believe you our dearest friend wouldn't tell us first what was going on in your life." Margie my other friend said "I feel the same way. Ann why on earth did we have to hear about this from Ray?" "Margie and Carol I don't know what you're talking about" I said. "Oh don't be ashamed" said Margie. "We know you must have some good reason and we're waiting to hear it." "No I don't have any reason because I'm not moving" I said. "Ray that prankster must have been trying to play a joke on us" said Carol.

     Unit 4, Capitalization and Punctuation

Using Quotation Marks and Apostrophes

> - Use **quotation marks** to show the exact words of a speaker. Use a comma or another punctuation mark to separate the quotation from the rest of the sentence.
>   EXAMPLES: "Do you have a book on helicopters?" asked Tom.
>   James said, "It's right here."
> - A quotation may be placed at the beginning or at the end of a sentence. It may also be divided within the sentence.
>   EXAMPLES: Deborah said, "There are sixty active members."
>   "Morton," asked Juanita, "have you read this magazine article?"

A. Add quotation marks and other punctuation where needed in the sentences below.

1. Dan, did you ever play football asked Tim.

2. Morris asked Why didn't you come in for an interview?

3. I have never said Laurie heard a story about a ghost.

4. Selina said Yuri thank you for the present.

5. When do we start on our trip to the mountains asked Stan.

6. Our guest said You don't know how happy I am to be in your house.

7. My sister said Sima bought those beautiful baskets in Mexico.

8. I'm going to plant the spinach said Doris as soon as I get home.

> - Use an **apostrophe** in a contraction to show where a letter or letters have been taken out.
>   EXAMPLES: Amelia **didn't** answer the phone. **I've** found my wallet.
> - Use an apostrophe to form a possessive noun. Add -'s to most singular nouns. Add -' to most plural nouns. Add -'s to a few nouns that have irregular plurals.
>   EXAMPLES: A **child's** toy was in our yard. The **girls'** toys were in our yard. The **children's** toys were in our yard.

B. After each sentence below, write the word in which an apostrophe has been left out. Add the apostrophe where needed.

1. Many players uniforms are red. _____

2. That dog played with the babys shoe. _____

3. Akira isnt coming with us to the library. _____

4. Its very warm for a fall day _____

5. The captains ship was one of the newest. _____

6. Marcia doesnt sing as well as my sister does. _____

7. Mens coats are sold in the new store. _____

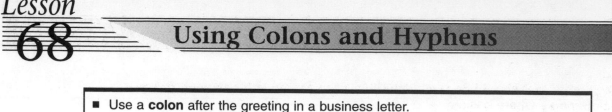

- Use a **colon** after the greeting in a business letter.
  EXAMPLES: Dear Sir: Dear Ms. Franklin:
- Use a colon between the hour and the minute when writing time.
  EXAMPLES: 2:00   7:45   9:37
- Use a colon to introduce a list.
  EXAMPLE: The suitcase contained these items: a toothbrush, a brush, a comb, and some clothing.

A. Add colons where needed in the sentences or phrases below.

1. The program begins at 8 3 0.

2. Dear Mrs. Zarins

3. These are the students who must return library books Julia Turner, Carl Porter, Crystal Fletcher, and Asako Satoshi.

4. Beverly wakes up every morning at 6 1 5.

5. Dear Mr. Graham

- Use a **hyphen** between the parts of some compound words.
  EXAMPLES: father-in-law   blue-black   well-known
            thirty-six   part-time   one-fourth
- Use a hyphen to separate the syllables of a word that is carried over from one line to the next.
  EXAMPLE: After eating dinner, we watched a television show about tornadoes.

B. Add hyphens where needed in the sentences below.

1. A driving safety expert will visit the school to give a presen tation on seat belts.

2. There should be forty two people at the lecture.

3. I searched high and low, but I couldn't seem to find that new, yellow zip per I bought today.

4. My mother in law is coming from British Columbia.

5. In fifty eight years of driving, he has a nearly perfect record.

6. Ralph and Victor came late to the meeting, but Lora and Angela arrived ear ly and stayed late.

7. George could lift weights with ease, and Alberto was able to swim twenty one laps without stopping.

8. Our air conditioning unit broke on the hottest day of this summer.

9. Donna had to go inside to change her clothes because Scoot, her frisky pup py, got his muddy paws on her.

A. Circle each letter that should be capitalized. Write the capital letter above it. Place punctuation marks where needed.

1. have you seen shelly today _____

2. is major bill brandon your cousin _____

3. mr. and mrs. john bell live at the ambassador apartments _____

4. *alices adventures in wonderland* by lewis carroll is an

   excellent book _____

5. how do people travel in the deserts of egypt _____

6. *heidi* was written by johanna spyri _____

7. i cant wait to spend Christmas in victoria with uncle will and aunt lee _____

8. casa loma was the beautiful home of sir henry pellat in

   toronto, ontario _____

9. *jungle book* was written by rudyard kipling _____

10. british columbia produces more fruit than any other province in canada _____

11. i am sure she lives at 203 brock ave replied sandra _____

12. mr. baldwin you won a trip to bermuda _____

13. o canada was written by calixa lavallée _____

14. mrs. perkins told us many interesting stories from inuit haida and

    algonquian mythology _____

15. isnt mount everest the highest mountain in the world _____

16. have you ever crossed the rocky mountains _____

17. how many kilometres does the st. lawrence river flow _____

18. one hundred french tourists were on the guided tour of ottawa, ont. _____

19. sometime i want to visit mexico city _____

20. carol r. brink wrote a book about a boy in scotland _____

21. the first monday in september is known as labour day _____

22. the olympic team will leave for paris, france, on thanksgiving day _____

B. Add commas where needed in the sentences below.

1. Tom do you know where the paper pencils and test forms are?

2. "We really enjoyed our trip through England Scotland and Wales" said Mr. Shaw.

3. I gave Angela my niece a pair of skates for her birthday and her parents gave her a radio.

4. "Jason please wash dry and fold the laundry for me" said Connie.

5. Dr. Wells our family doctor is retiring but Dr. Hernandez will take over her practice.

6. Yes I think Ms. Lawson my supervisor is a courteous capable and fair person.

7. I want to go to the beach on our vacation but my friend wants to go camping hiking and fishing.

8. Do you want to go to a movie or play cards Sharonda?

9. Mr. Coe my English instructor said "Make sure your reports are neat concise and accurate."

10. Dawn told Ms. Kim a nurse about Kelsey's fever.

11. James will mow the yard trim the hedge and water the flowers.

12. Sara Powell the lawyer will take the case.

C. Add quotation marks, apostrophes, colons, or hyphens where needed in the sentences below.

1. My mother in law said, Marys aunt will join us for dinner at 7 3 0.

2. Shanthi couldnt find the following items for her trip suntan lotion, her hat, and the keys to the cabin.

3. Ira, asked Linda, will you please bring forty eight cookies for the clubs bake sale?

4. Ms. Tysons secretary began the letter with Dear Sir i am writing on behalf of Ms. Tyson.

5. Scott said, Im going to Jims house tonight at 8 0 0 to help him finish his sons desk.

6. Megs friends gave her many gifts at her goodbye party a new shirt, two headbands, stationery, and a roll of stamps.

7. Mike and Todd dont have to go to bed until 9 3 0, said Larry.

8. Mr. Reids son is only twenty one years old and is already a well known figure in the com munity.

9. Rita said, The beautiful memorial fountain is near the parks main entrance.

10. Wont you be taking the coachs extra credit class? asked Eric.

11. Stephanies party begins at 8 3 0.

12. What time is your appointment, Jack? asked Diane.

 Unit 4, Capitalization and Punctuation

Using What You've Learned

A. Correct the stories below. Circle each letter that should be capitalized. Add missing periods, question marks, exclamation points, commas, quotation marks, colons, apostrophes, or hyphens where needed. Be sure to write the correct end punctuation on the blank after each sentence.

one of aesops fables is called "the fox and the crow _____ " it tells about a crow that stole a piece of cheese _____ the crow landed on the branch of a tree put the cheese in its mouth and began to eat it _____ but a fox was also interested in the cheese _____ it sat under the branch and thought about eating the cheese, too _____

the fox said crow i compliment you on your size beauty and strength _____ you would be the queen of all birds if you had a voice _____

caw exclaimed the crow _____

well the crow dropped the cheese _____ the fox pounced on it carried it off a few feet and then turned around _____

my friend said the fox you have every good quality except common sense _____

_____

our neighbour denise baldwin likes to tell me funny stories _____ one hot friday afternoon in august she told me about her trip to winnipeg, manitoba _____ she was walking out of a store with some presents she had bought for pat her sister _____ they were three joke gifts which included the following birthday candles that didnt blow out a silly hat and a mustache attached to some glasses _____ denise accidentally bumped into another shopper _____

im so sorry exclaimed denise _____

are you hurt asked the other shopper _____

no im not hurt said denise _____ both shoppers had dropped their presents and they bent over to pick them up _____

im denise baldwin she said as she picked up the presents _____

my name is carol schwartz said the other shopper _____

both shoppers said they were sorry again and then went on their way _____

denise gave her sister the presents when she returned to cobalt, saskatchewan _____ pat had a puzzled look on her face when she unwrapped them _____ the packages contained a rattle a bib and a baby bonnet _____

oh gasped denise i must have picked up the wrong presents when i bumped into ms. schwartz _____

whos ms. Schwartz asked pat _____

denise laughed and said i hope shes someone who likes joke gifts _____

B. Rewrite the story below. Be sure to use capital letters and punctuation marks where they are needed.

abigail hoffman one of canadas greatest women ath

letes was born in toronto, ontario in 1947 _____ in 1956 when she was

nine she started playing on a boys hockey team _____ because her hair

was short, everyone on the team thought she was a boy _____ her

teammates the other players and her coach were all fooled _____ they

only found out the truth when she was chosen to play on the leagues all-

star team and had to show her birth certificate _____

abby went on to have a brilliant career in sports _____ at fifteen she

won a middle-distance race at the national championships _____ abby

won gold medals in running twice at the pan-american games and once at

the 1966 commonwealth games _____ she participated in the olympics

four times _____ after she stopped competing she became the head of

sports canada _____

_____

_____

_____

_____

_____

_____

_____

_____

_____

_____

_____

_____

_____

_____

_____

_____

_____

_____

Unit 4, Capitalization and Punctuation

Writing Sentences

> - Every sentence has a base consisting of a simple subject and a simple predicate.
>   EXAMPLE: <u>Dolphins</u> <u>leap</u>.
> - Expand the meaning of a sentence by adding adjectives, adverbs, and prepositional phrases to the sentence base.
>   EXAMPLE: **The sleek** dolphins **suddenly** leap **high into the air**.

A. Expand the meaning of each sentence base by adding adjectives, adverbs, and/or prepositional phrases. Write each expanded sentence.

1. (Dinner cooks.) _____

2. (Clown chuckled.) _____

3. (Car raced.) _____

4. (Dancer spun.) _____

5. (Panthers growled.) _____

6. (Leaves fall.) _____

7. (Bread baked.) _____

8. (Lake glistened.) _____

9. (Ship glides.) _____

B. Write five sentence bases. Then write an expanded sentence containing each sentence base.

1. _____

   _____

2. _____

   _____

3. _____

   _____

4. _____

   _____

5. _____

   _____

Writing Topic Sentences

> ■ A **topic sentence** is the sentence within a paragraph that states the main idea. It is often placed at the beginning of a paragraph.
>
> EXAMPLE:
>
> **The trip to the national park was a great success**. First, the visitors learned a lot from their guide about the park. They learned that the forest was created by people, not by nature. To their surprise, they found out that the park had more than five hundred species of plants. Then they went on a hike and even spotted a falcon flying overhead. Finally, the visitors had a wonderful picnic lunch and headed back home.

A. Write a topic sentence for each paragraph below.

1.   Some jewellery is made out of feathers, leather, shells, or wood. Other jewellery is crafted from gold, silver, brass, copper, or other metals. Gems and unusual stones are added for their beauty and value.

    Topic Sentence: _____

2.   A pet goldfish needs clean water. A pump should be placed in the water to supply fresh air. The water temperature must be constant, and it must not go below 27°C (80°F). The goldfish should be fed flaked fish food or small insects.

    Topic Sentence: _____

3.   When Jana crawls over to a kitchen cabinet, she whips the door open to see what's behind it. With a little help from Jana, the pots and pans are on the floor in no time. If she sees a bag of groceries, Jana has to investigate the contents. After she is tucked in bed for the night, this toddler loves to climb out of her crib and explore.

    Topic Sentence: _____

B. Write a topic sentence for each of the paragraph ideas below.

1. birthday parties _____

2. a great adventure _____

3. a great Canadian _____

4. a favourite holiday_____

5. homework _____

6. video games _____

7. vacations _____

8. the Olympics _____

> ■ The idea expressed in a topic sentence can be developed with sentences containing **supporting details**. Details can include facts, examples, and reasons.

A. Read the topic sentence below. Then read the sentences that follow. Circle the seven sentences that contain details that support the topic sentence.

Topic Sentence: The CNE is a wonderful place to go for a fun-filled day.

1. The roller coaster is the most popular ride in the park.
2. The CNE is the world's largest annual exhibition.
3. You can test your pitching skills at the game booths.
4. You can win a stuffed animal at one of the pitching games.
5. Young children can enjoy a part of the park made especially for them.
6. We had sandwiches and potato salad for lunch.
7. The exhibitions in the Horticultural Building are always interesting.
8. You can even see the latest in computer technology at the Ex.
9. What do you like to do during summer vacation?
10. The ferris wheel gives a great view of the lake from high in the air.

B. Choose one of the topic sentences below. Write it on the first line. Then write five sentences that contain supporting details. The details can be facts, examples, or reasons.

1. Exercise is important for maintaining good health.
2. Being the oldest child in a family has its advantages.
3. The teenage years are a time of change.
4. True friendship makes life more interesting and fun.

Topic and Audience

- The **topic** of a paragraph is the subject of the paragraph.
- The **title** of a paragraph should be based on the topic.
- The **audience** is the person or persons who will read the paragraph.
  EXAMPLES: teachers, classmates, readers of the school newspaper, friends, family members

---

A. Suppose that you chose the topic <u>watching TV</u>. Underline the sentence that you would choose for the topic sentence.

1. Watching TV is one of the best ways to learn about things.

2. Watching TV is a waste of time.

3. The time children spend watching TV should be limited.

B. Think about the topic sentence you chose in Exercise A. Then underline the audience for whom you would like to write.

1. your friends

2. your family members

3. readers of a newspaper

C. Write a paragraph beginning with the topic sentence you chose in Exercise A. Keep your audience in mind as you write. Be sure to write a title.

_____

_____

_____

_____

_____

_____

_____

_____

_____

_____

_____

- **Note-taking** is an important step when writing a report.
- You can find information for reports in encyclopedias, books, and magazines.
- Before you begin, organize your research questions.
- Write information accurately and in your own words.
- Take more notes than you expect to need, so you won't have to go back to your sources a second time.

A. Underline a topic below that interests you.

1. a favourite hobby
2. the stars or planets
3. a historical figure
4. a species of animal
5. movies

6. a favourite sport
7. a favourite food
8. fashion or costumes
9. gardening
10. airplanes

B. Gather some sources of information about your topic. Write the name of your topic on the first line below. For example, if you have chosen "a favourite food," you might write the name of that particular food. Then write notes about the topic on the remaining lines.

_____

_____

_____

_____

_____

_____

_____

_____

_____

_____

_____

_____

_____

_____

- Organize your thoughts before writing by making an **outline**. An outline consists of the title of the topic, **main headings** for the main ideas, and **subheadings** for the supporting ideas.
- Main headings are listed after Roman numerals. Subheadings are listed after capital letters.

Topic: First aid for burns
Main heading   I. Keeping the wound clean
Subheadings {   A. Applying thick, clean dressing
             B. Avoiding sprays or oils
       II. Easing pain
          A. Applying ice packs
          B. Putting injured area in ice water

- **Write an outline for the topic you chose in Exercise A on page 99. Use the sample outline as a guide.**

Topic: _____

     I. _____

        A. _____

        B. _____

     II. _____

        A. _____

        B. _____

    III. _____

        A. _____

        B. _____

    IV. _____

        A. _____

        B. _____

     V. _____

        A. _____

        B. _____

Writing a Report

> ■ A **report** is a series of informative paragraphs covering a main topic.
> Each paragraph has a topic sentence and other sentences that contain
> supporting details. Begin with a paragraph that introduces the report,
> and end with a paragraph that concludes the report.

A. Read the paragraphs below.

Exploring the Mystery Planets: Uranus, Neptune, and Pluto

The planets Uranus, Neptune, and Pluto are difficult to study because of their distance from Earth. However, scientists are not completely without information about these planets. They know, for example, that Uranus is more than twice as far from Earth as Saturn is. They also know that Neptune is half again as far from Earth as Uranus. Both Saturn and Uranus are four times the size of Earth.

Scientists have explored the mysteries of Uranus. As Uranus orbits the sun every 84 years, it rolls around on its side. Although it is larger than Earth and orbits the sun more slowly, Uranus spins on its axis very rapidly. It completes a full rotation in 15 hours, 30 minutes. Five known satellites accompany Uranus, along with a system of nine dark rings that were discovered in 1977. The diameter of Uranus is 52 200 kilometres (32 500 miles), and the planet lies 2.87 billion kilometres (1.78 billion miles) from the sun. Because of this great distance, the temperature of Uranus is -220°C (-360°F), far too cold for any earth creature to survive.

Scientists have also explored the mysteries of Neptune. At a distance of 4.5 billion kilometres (2.8 billion miles) from the sun, Neptune appears through a telescope as a greenish-blue disk. Neptune is somewhat smaller than Uranus, having a diameter of about 48 000 kilometres (30 000 miles). It is also very cold (-200°C, or -328°F). Two of Neptune's satellites have been named Nereid and Triton. In the summer of 1989, *Voyager 2* finally passed Neptune and, among other things, revealed that there are up to five rings around the planet.

It was 1930 before Pluto, the last planet in our solar system, was discovered. The "new" planet is 6 billion kilometres (3.67 billion miles) from the sun and takes 248 years to complete its orbit. In comparison, Earth takes only 365 days to complete a single orbit. While Pluto has not been measured exactly, scientists believe that it has a diameter of 2670 kilometres (1600 miles).

There are more interesting facts about Pluto. It also has a satellite, called Charon, which is five times closer to Pluto than our moon is to Earth. The yellowish colour of Pluto indicates that it has very little atmosphere. Pluto's distance from the sun indicates that its climate is the coldest of the nine planets in our solar system.

Many mysteries remain concerning Uranus, Neptune, and Pluto, despite the fact that so much has been discovered. The questioning minds of the twenty-first century will continue our search for the secrets of space.

B. Circle the word or phrase that best completes each statement about this report.

1. Most of the report's supporting details are (facts, examples, reasons).

2. The writer of this report has included the (colour, discoverer, diameter) of each of the three planets.

3. The writer does not discuss the relationship of the mystery planets to (Earth, Mars, the sun).

C. Underline the topic sentence in each paragraph.

Lesson 76

Revising and Proofreading

- **Revising** gives you a chance to rethink and review what you have written and to improve your writing. Revise by adding words and information, by taking out unneeded words and information, and by moving words, sentences, and paragraphs around.
- **Proofreading** has to do with checking spelling, punctuation, grammar, and capitalization. Use proofreader's marks to show changes needed in your writing.

Proofreader's Marks

≡	⊙	ⓢⓟ
Capitalize.	Add a period.	Correct spelling.
/	∧	¶
Make a small letter.	Add something.	Indent for new paragraph.
⌄	℘	→
Add a comma.	Take something out.	Move something.

A. Rewrite the paragraph below. Correct the errors by following the proofreader's marks.

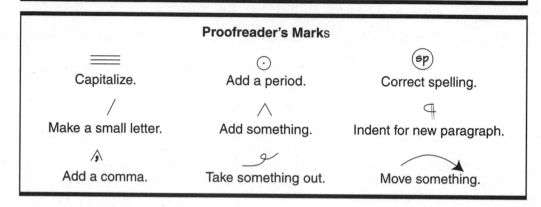

banff national park is the oldest Park national in canada It is located in the rocky mountains in alberta, West of calgary. the hot springs that were discovered in 1885 were the reson the government desided to perfect land the. now the park covers 6600 Kilometres square, and attracts hikers, skiiers, and campers it is one of 34 national parks across Canada, which cover an Area about the size of england.

_____

_____

B. Read the paragraphs below. Use proofreader's marks to revise and proofread the paragraphs. Then write your revised paragraphs below.

althow most parks are set aside for peoples' enjoyment, other national national parks are useful to Some speices of animals as well also. wood bufalo national park is the largest national park in the country it was crated in 1922 as a haven for the wood bison, which was almost Extinct. Now there are more than 4000 bison in the park. a heard of plains Bison wer also moved to the Pertection of the park in the 1920s.

other animals choose the park as a refuje all by themsilves. in 1954, a Bush Pilot came across the breeding grounds of the whooping crane it was in wood buffalo park. until then, no one know where these burds nested how they lived or how to help them

There were only 21 whooping left in 1941. Now Sientists are trying to help them to Breed. But they are still Endangered. There are about 160 wild whooping cranes today. they spend the Summers in Buffalo Wood national park, and the winters in Aransas national wildlife Refuge in texas.

_____

_____

_____

_____

_____

_____

_____

_____

_____

_____

_____

_____

_____

_____

- A **business letter** has six parts.
  - The **heading** contains the address of the person writing and the date.
  - The **inside address** contains the name and address of the person to whom the letter is written.
  - The **greeting** tells to whom the letter is written. Use "Dear Sir or Madam" if you are unsure who will read the letter. Use a colon after the greeting in a business letter.
  - The **body** is the message of the letter. It should be brief, courteous, and to the point.
  - The **closing** is the ending that follows the body.
  - The **signature** is the name of the person who is writing the letter.
- When writing a business letter, remember the following:
  - Use business-size paper and envelopes.
  - Centre your letter on the page, leaving at least a 2.5 cm margin on each side.
  - Include specific information, such as quantities, sizes, numbers, brands, prices, manner of shipment, and amount of payment.
  - When you have finished, reread your letter. Rewrite it if you are not satisfied with any part of it.

A. Study this business letter. Then answer the questions below.

heading	572 Avenue Dupont La Tuque, PQ G9X 2P2 April 4, 1997
inside address	Order Department Perfection Computer Company 9940 Main Street Hamilton, ON L8M 2R6

greeting
body
	Dear Sir or Madam:
	      Please send me one copy of *Making Friends With Your Computer*. Enclosed is $16.95 to cover the cost of the book plus shipping and handling.
	      Thank you for your assistance.

closing	Sincerely yours,
signature	*Chris Morrow* Chris Morrow

1. Who wrote the letter? _____

2. What is the greeting? _____

3. Where is Perfection Computer Company located? _____

_____

4. When was the letter written? _____

■ Use a business-size envelope for a business letter. Be sure to include your return address. Check both addresses to be sure they are correct.

Chris Morrow
572 Avenue Dupont
La Tuque, P.Q. G9X 2P2

Order Department
Perfection Computer Company
9940 Main Street
Hamilton, ON L8M 2R6

B. **Write a brief business letter asking for information about the Halifax Explosion that you can use in a report. Write to the Maritime Museum of the Atlantic at 1675 Lower Water Street in Halifax, Nova Scotia. The postal code is B3J 1S4. Then circle the parts of the letter that would appear on the envelope.**

A. Write expanded sentences by adding adjectives, adverbs, and/or prepositional phrases to each sentence below.

1. (Whistle blew.) _____

2. (Cowhand rode.) _____

3. (Fire trucks roared.) _____

B. Write a possible topic sentence for each topic below.

1. friendship _____

2. zoos _____

C. Write a topic sentence for each paragraph below.

1. Trees provide shade from the sun and block the wind. They provide homes and food for many animals. Trees are the source of wood for thousands of useful products.

   Topic Sentence: _____

2. Dogs help police officers find criminals and illegal substances. They guard homes and businesses. Some dogs help people with disabilities live more independent lives.

   Topic Sentence: _____

D. Circle the letters for the sentences that contain details that support the topic sentences below.

1. **Topic Sentence:** Rockets have many peacetime uses.

   a. They are used to signal that a ship is in trouble.

   b. High-performance rockets must have large nozzles.

   c. Rockets carry cables across rivers for the construction of bridges.

2. **Topic Sentence:** Computers are very useful in schools.

   a. They are used to help students practise reading, writing, and math skills.

   b. Teachers keep records on computers.

   c. Computers can be used to store a great deal of information.

3. **Topic Sentence:** Our first camping trip was a disaster.

   a. We all got poison ivy while fishing in a nearby stream.

   b. We set up our tents in a camping area.

   c. Our campground had to be evacuated because of a large brushfire.

E. Read the following paragraphs. Take notes, and make an outline from the information.

The Moon

The moon is Earth's closest neighbour in space. It is about 382 000 kilometres away. The moon is about one-fourth the size of the earth. It has a diameter of about 3456 kilometres.

The moon is always moving in space. It revolves around Earth in an oval path. The moon completes one revolution in about 27 1/3 days. The moon also rotates, or turns on its axis, as it revolves around the earth. It takes one month for the moon to revolve around Earth.

Notes

_____

_____

_____

Outline

I. _____

   A. _____

   B. _____

   C. _____

II. _____

   A. _____

   B. _____

F. Find ten spelling, punctuation, and grammar errors in the paragraph below. Use the proofreader's marks on page 102 to mark the errors.

Flying a kite can be fun, but it can also serve some practical purposes. For

example, Benjamin franklin uses a kite in his experiments with electricity. In the

early part of the twentieth century, box kites carring instruments measured wind

speed temperature pressure and and humidity. they were also used to lift soldiers

to hieghts where they could see the enemy. Today they serve as signals in

air-see-rescue operations.

G. Number the six parts of a business letter in the order in which they appear in a letter.

_____ **1.** body   _____ **3.** heading   _____ **5.** greeting

_____ **2.** closing   _____ **4.** inside address   _____ **6.** signature

A. Write a report about the topic you chose on page 99. Use your outline and notes in writing the report. Be sure to write an interesting topic sentence for each paragraph and to use supporting details. Keep your audience in mind as you write. You may use the report on page 101 as a model. You might need to use your own paper.

B. Proofread and revise the report you wrote on page 108. Write your revised report below. You might need to use your own paper.

_____

_____

_____

_____

_____

_____

_____

_____

_____

_____

_____

_____

_____

_____

_____

_____

_____

_____

_____

_____

_____

_____

© 1997 Gage Educational Publishing Company

Dictionary: Guide Words

- A **dictionary** is a reference book that contains definitions of words and other information about their history and use.
- **Entries** in a dictionary are listed in **alphabetical order**.
- **Guide words** appear at the top of each dictionary page. Guide words show the first and last entry on the page.
    EXAMPLE: The word dog would appear on a dictionary page with the guide words dodge / doll. The word dull would not.

A. Put a check in front of each word that would be listed on the dictionary page with the given guide words.

1. frozen / gather

_____ fruit

_____ grain

_____ furnish

_____ gate

_____ gallon

_____ former

_____ forgive

_____ fuzz

_____ galaxy

_____ future

2. money / muscle

_____ muddy

_____ moss

_____ motorcycle

_____ mustard

_____ moisten

_____ moose

_____ museum

_____ morning

_____ mortal

_____ modest

3. perfect / pin

_____ perfume

_____ pit

_____ pick

_____ photo

_____ pest

_____ plastic

_____ pillow

_____ pile

_____ pipe

_____ pizza

B. Number the words in each column in the order in which they would appear in a dictionary. Then write the words that could be the guide words for each column.

1. _____ / _____

_____ raccoon

_____ radar

_____ rabbit

_____ raisin

_____ react

_____ reflect

_____ rebel

_____ rainfall

_____ relay

_____ remind

_____ refuse

_____ ran

2. _____ / _____

_____ seize

_____ shellfish

_____ shrink

_____ signal

_____ silent

_____ scent

_____ shuffle

_____ shaft

_____ serpent

_____ seldom

_____ scope

_____ selfish

3. _____ / _____

_____ octopus

_____ olive

_____ of

_____ office

_____ old

_____ odour

_____ once

_____ oil

_____ odd

_____ onion

_____ occasion

_____ only

Unit 6, Study Skills

- A **syllable** is a part of a word that is pronounced at one time. Dictionary entry words are divided into syllables to show how they can be divided at the end of a writing line.
- A **midline dot** (·) is placed between syllables to separate them.
  EXAMPLE: man·a·ger
- If a word has a beginning or ending syllable of only one letter, do not divide it so that one letter stands alone.
  EXAMPLES: a·lone   sand·y

A. Write each word as a whole word.

1. ad·ver·tise _____

2. blun·der _____

3. par·a·dise _____

4. mis·chie·vous _____

5. con·crete _____

6. mi·cro·phone _____

7. in·ci·dent _____

8. val·ue _____

B. Find each word in a dictionary. Rewrite the word, placing a midline dot between each syllable.

1. bicycle _____

2. solution _____

3. category _____

4. punishment _____

5. behaviour _____

6. quarterback _____

7. disappear _____

8. theory _____

9. wonderful _____

10. biology _____

11. sizzle _____

12. foreign _____

13. transparent _____

14. civilization _____

C. Write two ways in which each word may be divided at the end of a writing line.

1. mosquito _____mos·quito_____   _____mosqui·to_____

2. ambition _____   _____

3. boundary _____   _____

4. gingerbread _____   _____

5. geography _____   _____

6. leadership _____   _____

Lesson
80

Dictionary: Pronunciation

- Each dictionary entry word is followed by a respelling that shows how the word is **pronounced**.
- **Accent marks** (´) show which syllable or syllables are said with extra stress.
  EXAMPLE: hope·ful (hōp′ fəl)
- A **pronunciation key** (shown below) explains the other symbols used in the respellings.

A. Use the pronunciation key to answer the questions.

hat, āge, fär; let, ēqual, tėrm; it, īce; hot, ōpen, ôrder; oil, out; cup, pút, rüle; əbove, takən, pencəl, lemən, circəs; ch, child; ng, long; sh, ship; th, thin; ŦH, then; zh, measure

1. Which word contains an <u>a</u> that is pronounced the same

   as the <u>a</u> in <u>apple</u>? _____

2. How many words are given for the symbol ə? _____

3. Think of another word that contains the sound of ə.

   _____

4. What symbol represents the sound of the <u>s</u> in <u>pleasure</u>? _____

5. What is the symbol for the pronunciation of <u>oo</u> in <u>boot</u>? _____

6. What is the symbol for the pronunciation of <u>th</u> in <u>themselves</u>? _____

B. Use the pronunciation key to help you choose the correct word for each respelling. Underline the correct word.

1.	(ə lĭv′)	olive	live	alive
2.	(lōd)	load	lead	loud
3.	(trü)	threw	true	try
4.	(thik)	thick	trick	tick
5.	(fol ən)	fallen	falling	fooling
6.	(kāp)	cap	cop	cape
7.	(īs)	is	ice	as
8.	(ŦHā)	that	they	the
9.	(sup′ ər)	super	support	supper
10.	(lok′ ər)	locker	looker	lock
11.	(hōm)	hum	hem	home
12.	(fot)	fought	fat	fit
13.	(mĭt)	mitt	meet	might
14.	(fül)	full	fuel	fool
15.	(frēz)	froze	free	freeze
16.	(let′ is)	lettuce	let's	less

Unit 6, Study Skills

- A dictionary lists the **definitions** of each entry word. Many words have more than one definition. In this case, the most commonly used definition is given first. Sometimes a definition is followed by a sentence showing a use of the entry word.
- A dictionary also gives the **part of speech** for each entry word. An abbreviation (shown below) stands for each part of speech. Some words might be used as more than one part of speech.
  - EXAMPLE: **frost** (frost) *n.* **1** frozen moisture. *There was frost on all the leaves.* *-v.* **2** to cover with frosting: *I'll frost the cake when it's cool.*

- **Use the dictionary samples below to answer the questions.**

spec·i·fy (spes´ ə fī´) *v.* **1** mention or name definitely: *Did you specify any particular time for us to call?* **2** include in the SPECIFICATIONS: *The contractor couldn't use shingles because slate was specified.*

spec·i·men (spes´ə mən) *n.* **1** one of a group or class taken to show what the others are like: *a fine specimen of French art.* **2** regarded as a specimen, for medical purposes.

speck·le (spek´əl) *n.* a small spot or mark: *This hen is grey with white speckles.* *-v.* mark with speckles.

spec·tac·u·lar (spek tak´yə lər) *adj.* **1** making a great display: *The television program included a spectacular scene of a storm.* **2** having to do with a spectacle or show. *-n.* a spectacular display or show.

1. Which word can be used as either a noun or a verb? _____

2. Which word can be used only as a verb?

   _____

3. Which word can be used only as a noun?

   _____

n.	noun
pron.	pronoun
v.	verb
adj.	adjective
adv.	adverb
prep.	preposition

4. Which word can be used either as a noun or as an adjective? _____

5. Write a sentence using the first definition of spectacular. _____

   _____

6. Write a sentence using the first definition of specify. _____

   _____

7. Write a sentence using speckle as a verb. _____

   _____

8. Use the second definition of specimen in a sentence. _____

   _____

9. Which word shows two definitions used as a noun? _____

   _____

Dictionary: Word Origins

> ■ An **etymology** is the origin and development of a word. Many dictionary entries include etymologies. The etymology is usually enclosed in brackets ⟨ ⟩.
>
> EXAMPLE: **repair** ⟨ME < L *reparare* < *re-* again + *parare* prepare⟩. The word *repair* first appeared in Middle English, taken from Latin *reparare* meaning *re-* again + *parare* prepare.

■ **Use these dictionary entries to answer the questions.**

chaise longue (shāz´long´) *n.* a couchlike chair with a long seat, in which a person can sit with outstretched legs. ⟨<F *chaise longue* long chair⟩

cam·pus (kam´pəs) *n.* **1** the grounds and buildings of a university, college, or school. **2** the grounds and buildings of a factory, hospital, etc. ⟨<L *campus* field, plain ⟩

gar·de·nia (gär dē´nyə *or* gär dē´nē ə) *n.* any of a large genus (*Gardenia*) of tropical and subtropical trees and shrubs, having fragrant, roselike, white or yellow flowers with waxy petals. ⟨<NL; after Alexander *Garden* (1730-1791), an American botanist⟩

pas·teur·ize (pas´chə rīz´) *v.* heat (milk, beer, etc.) to a high temperature and chill it quickly to destroy

harmful bacteria without causing a major chemical change to the substance itself. ⟨after Louis *Pasteur* (1822-1895), a French chemist⟩

ut·ter (ut´ər) *v.* speak; make known; express ⟨ME *uttren*, literally, put forth < OE *ūtor*, comparative of *ūt* out⟩

wam·pum (wom´pəm) *n.* **1** beads made from polished shells (*Venus mercenaria*) strung in belts and sashes, formerly used by eastern First Nations peoples as money, as a reminder of a treaty, and as ornament. The white form was more common, but the black or dark purple was of greater value. **2** *Slang.* money. ⟨<Algonquian: Narraganset *wampompeag* strings of white (things) 124⟩

1. Which word comes from an Algonquian word? _____

2. What does the Algonquian word mean? _____

3. Which word was formed from the name of a chemist? _____

4. Which word comes from French words? _____

5. What do the French words chaise and longue mean? _____

6. Which word was formed from the name of a botanist? _____

7. Which word is short for the word wampompeag? _____

8. Which words come from Latin words? _____

9. Which word comes from a Middle English word? _____

10. Which word comes from two languages? _____

11. What does the word uttren mean? _____

12. What does the Latin word campus mean? _____

13. Which word is the name of a flower? _____

14. Which word names a piece of furniture? _____

- A **title page** lists the name of a book and its author.
- A **copyright page** tells who published the book, where it was published, and when it was published.
- A **table of contents** lists the chapter or unit titles and the page numbers on which they begin. It is at the front of a book.
- An **index** gives a detailed list of the topics in a book and the page numbers on which each topic is found. It is in the back of a book.

A. Answer the questions below.

1. Where would you look to find when a book was published? _____

2. Where would you look to find the page number of a particular topic? _____

3. Where would you look to find the author's name? _____

4. Where would you look to find the titles of the chapters in a book? _____

B. Use your *Language Power* book to answer the questions.

1. When was this book published? _____

2. Who is the publisher? _____

3. Where is the publishing company located? _____

4. On what page does Unit 6 begin? _____

5. On what page does the lesson on nouns begin? _____

6. What lesson begins on page 104? _____

7. What pages teach capitalization? _____

8. What page teaches indefinite pronouns? _____

9. What lesson begins on page 6? _____

10. What is the name of Unit 1? _____

11. What is the title of lesson 24? _____

12. On what page does Unit 2 begin? _____

13. What is the name of Unit 6? _____

14. On what page does the Unit 5 Review begin? _____

15. What is the title of lesson 38? _____

- Books on library shelves are arranged by **call numbers**. Each book is assigned a number from 000 to 999, according to its subject matter.
- The main subject groups for call numbers are as follows:

000-099 Reference	500-599 Science and Math
100-199 Philosophy	600-699 Technology
200-299 Religion	700-799 The Arts
300-399 Social Sciences	800-899 Literature
400-499 Languages	900-999 History and Geography

A. **Write the call number group in which you would find each book.**

1. *A Guide to Electronics in a New Age* _____

2. *A Traveller's Handbook of Everyday German* _____

3. *1994 World Almanac and Book of Facts* _____

4. *A History of the Roman Empire* _____

5. *The Modern Philosophers* _____

6. *Religions of the World* _____

7. *Solving Word Problems in Mathematics* _____

8. *Folktales of Norway* _____

9. *Painting with Watercolours* _____

10. *People in Society* _____

11. *Learn Spanish in Seven Days* _____

12. *Science Experiments for the Beginner* _____

13. *Technology in a New Century* _____

14. *Funny Poems for a Rainy Day* _____

15. *The Continent of Africa* _____

B. **Write the titles of three of your favourite non-fiction books. Write the call number group beside each title.**

1. _____

2. _____

3. _____

- The library catalogue contains information cards on every book in the library. Most libraries have their catalogues on computer, although some still use a card catalogue. The information is filed in the same manner in both online and card catalogues.
- Each book is filed in at least three ways. You can look under:
    1. the author's last name
    2. the subject of the book
    3. the title of the book

A. Use the sample catalogue entry to answer the questions.

Author Card

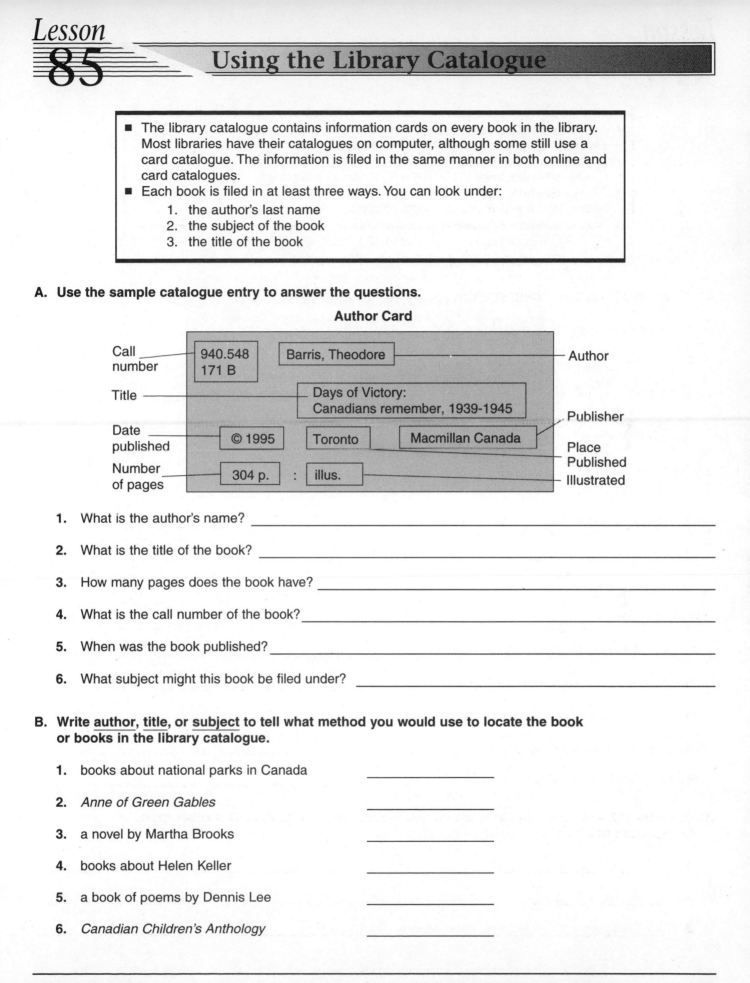

1. What is the author's name? _____

2. What is the title of the book? _____

3. How many pages does the book have? _____

4. What is the call number of the book? _____

5. When was the book published? _____

6. What subject might this book be filed under? _____

B. Write <u>author</u>, <u>title</u>, or <u>subject</u> to tell what method you would use to locate the book or books in the library catalogue.

1. books about national parks in Canada   _____

2. *Anne of Green Gables*   _____

3. a novel by Martha Brooks   _____

4. books about Helen Keller   _____

5. a book of poems by Dennis Lee   _____

6. *Canadian Children's Anthology*   _____

- An **encyclopedia** is a reference book that contains articles on many different subjects. The articles are arranged alphabetically in volumes. Each volume is marked to show which articles are inside.
- Guide words are used to show the first topic on each page.
- At the end of most articles there is a listing of cross-references to related topics for the reader to investigate.

- **Read each sample encyclopedia entry below. Then refer to each to answer the questions that follow.**

> **BANTING**, Sir Frederick (1891-1941), was one of the discoverers of insulin. Banting was born in Alliston, Ontario, and educated at the University of Toronto. In 1921-22, he and a team of researchers that included C.H. Best, J.J.R. Macleod, and J.B. Collip discovered insulin, and in doing so made available a treatment for diabetes mellitus. Banting received the Nobel Prize for his work. *See also* INSULIN; CHARLES BEST; DIABETES.

1. Whom is the article about? _____

2. When did he live? _____

3. Where did he go to university? _____

4. What is he best known for? _____

5. Who else did he work with? _____

6. What other articles in the encyclopedia are related to the subject? _____

> **INSULIN** is a natural substance produced by the special clusters of cells in the pancreas called the islets of Langėrhans. It regulates the amount of sugar in the blood. If these glucose levels are higher than normal, the individual will develop a disease called diabetes mellitus. Diabetes can be fatal if it is not treated with daily doses of insulin, which was discovered in 1922 by Sir Frederick Banting, Charles Best, and a team of researchers at the University of Toronto. Insulin does not cure diabetes, but it does allow sufferers to live much longer and more normal lives.

7. Why do you think this cross-reference is included in the article about Banting? _____

_____

_____

8. Does the above cross-reference mention Frederick Banting? _____

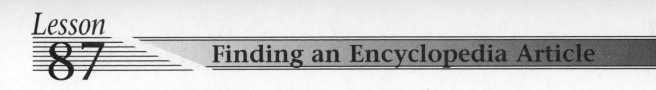

When looking for an article in the encyclopedia:
- Always look up the last name of a person.
   EXAMPLE: To find an article on Helen Keller, look under <u>Keller</u>.
- Look up the first word in the name of a city, province, or country.
   EXAMPLE: To find an article on Puerto Rico, look under <u>Puerto</u>.
- Look up the most specific word in the name of a geographical location.
   EXAMPLE: To find an article on Lake Erie, look under <u>Erie</u>.
- Look up the most significant word in the name of a general topic.
   EXAMPLE: To find an article on neon lamps, look under <u>neon</u>.

A. The example below shows how the volumes of a particular encyclopedia are marked to indicate the alphabetical range of the articles they cover. Write the number of the volume in which you would find each article.

A	B	C-CH	CI-CZ	D	E	F	G	H	I-J	K	L
1	2	3	4	5	6	7	8	9	10	11	12

M	N	O	P	Q-R	S-SH	SI-SZ	T	U-V	W-X-Y-Z
13	14	15	16	17	18	19	20	21	22

1. camping _____
2. North Dakota _____
3. Jonathan Swift _____
4. giant panda _____
5. Nova Scotia _____

6. John F. Kennedy _____
7. Mount Kilimanjaro _____
8. sand flea _____
9. New Guinea _____
10. Maurice Richard _____

11. Caspian Sea _____
12. Frontier College _____
13. Victor Hugo _____
14. elementary school _____
15. Lake Ontario _____

B. Look up the following articles in an encyclopedia. Write a cross-reference for each article.

1. bee _____
2. X-ray _____
3. atom _____
4. music _____

5. Alberta _____
6. space travel _____
7. Roberta Bondar _____
8. cartoon _____

C. Choose a person who interests you, and find the entry for that person in an encyclopedia. Then answer the questions below.

1. Who is the person you've chosen? _____

2. When did this person live? _____

3. What made this person famous? _____

4. What encyclopedia did you use? _____

Lesson 88

Using Visual Aids

- A **chart** lists information in columns, which you read down, and rows, which you read across. The information can be either words or numbers.
- A **graph** can show how quantities change over time. It often shows how two or more things change in relation to one another. The information can be shown through the use of lines, dots, bars, pictures, or circles.

A. Use the chart and graph to answer the following questions.

Exercise Chart

Person	Hours Spent Walking	Hours Spent Bicyciing
Julia	2	3
Ted	3	3
Miguel	0	6
Kiko	4	2
Terry	3	4

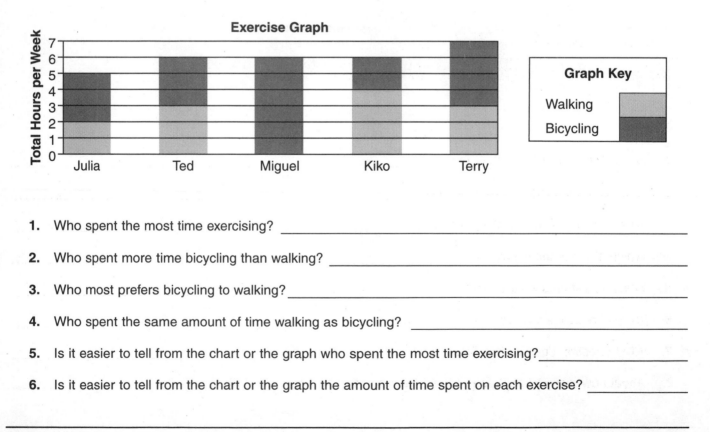

Exercise Graph

1. Who spent the most time exercising? _____

2. Who spent more time bicycling than walking? _____

3. Who most prefers bicycling to walking? _____

4. Who spent the same amount of time walking as bicycling? _____

5. Is it easier to tell from the chart or the graph who spent the most time exercising?_____

6. Is it easier to tell from the chart or the graph the amount of time spent on each exercise? _____

          Unit 6, Study Skills

- A **road map** is another valuable type of visual aid. Maps like the one shown below are helpful when you are unfamiliar with a certain area. To use any map, you should refer to its **legend**, **compass rose**, and **scale**.
- The legend tells what each symbol on the map represents.
- The compass rose is made up of arrows that point north, south, east, and west.
- The scale allows you to determine how far it is from one location to another. To use the scale, mark the distance between any two locations along the edge of a sheet of paper. Then place the sheet of paper alongside the scale of distance, lining up one of the marks with zero. This will allow you to read the distance between the two locations.

B. Use the map to answer the questions below.

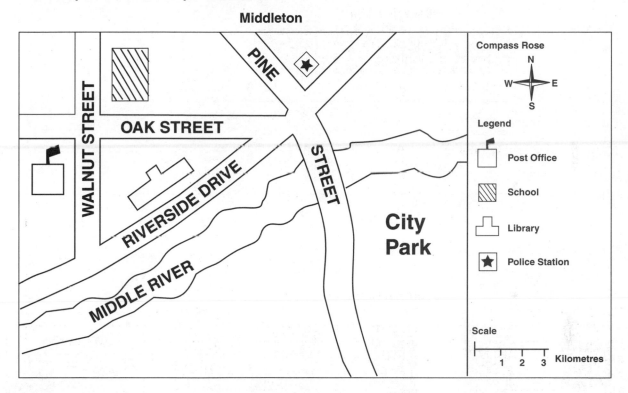

Middleton

1. Is City Park north or south of the river? _____

2. At which intersection is the post office? _____

3. What building is west of the police station? _____

4. Which street is the library on? _____

5. Which street crosses the river? _____

6. What direction is the school from the library? _____

7. What direction does Walnut Street run? _____

8. About how many kilometres is it from the post office to the police station? _____

■ A **thesaurus** is a reference book that writers use to find the exact words they need. Like a dictionary, a thesaurus lists its entry words alphabetically. Each entry word has a list of **synonyms**, or words that can be used in its place. Some thesauri also list **antonyms** for the entry word.

  EXAMPLE: You have just written the following sentence: The spectators **looked** from the sidelines.

  With the help of a thesaurus, you could improve the sentence by replacing <u>looked</u> with its more precise synonym <u>watched</u>.

The spectators **watched** from the sidelines.

A. **Use the thesaurus sample below to answer the questions.**

> **heat** *n.* **syn.** warmth, fire, flame, fever, emotion, glow, blush, redness. **ant.** cold, coolness, ice, chilliness

1. Which is the entry word? _____

2. What are its synonyms? _____

   _____

3. Which word would you use in place of <u>blaze</u>? _____

4. Which word would you use in place of <u>temperature</u>? _____

5. What are the antonyms of <u>heat</u>? _____

6. Which antonyms would you use in place of <u>hotness</u>? _____

7. What antonym would you use in place of <u>hot</u>? _____

B. **Write synonyms of <u>heat</u> to complete the sentences.**

1. Eleanor sat by the _____ in the fireplace.

2. Its _____ spread through her body as she relaxed.

3. She felt a warm _____ inside her.

4. Her skin began to show some _____ as she sat there longer.

5. She felt as if she had a _____ .

6. She moved farther away from the flickering _____ .

7. She looked in the mirror and saw the _____ on her face.

8. Happiness was the _____ she felt.

Lesson 90

Choosing Reference Sources

- Use a **dictionary** to find the definitions and pronunciations of words, suggestions for word usage, and etymologies.
- Use an **encyclopedia** to find articles about many different people, places, and other subjects. Also use an encyclopedia to find references to related topics.
- Use an **atlas** to find maps and other information about geographical locations.

- Write <u>encyclopedia</u>, <u>dictionary</u>, or <u>atlas</u> to show which source you would use to find the following information. Some topics might be found in more than one source.

1. the pronunciation of the word <u>measure</u> _____

2. the location of Wood Buffalo National Park _____

3. the care and feeding of a dog _____

4. the distance between Rome and Naples _____

5. jewellery throughout the ages _____

6. planning a vegetable garden _____

7. the meaning of the word <u>federal</u> _____

8. the etymology of the word <u>consider</u> _____

9. the early life of Sir Wilfrid Laurier _____

10. the states through which the Mississippi River flows _____

11. how volcanoes form _____

12. a definition of the word <u>ape</u> _____

13. the rivers and mountains of Mexico _____

14. how paper is made _____

15. the location of the border between India and Pakistan. _____

16. the history of kite making _____

17. the pronunciation of the word <u>particular</u> _____

18. the names of lakes in Northern B.C. _____

19. the meanings of the homographs of <u>bow</u> _____

20. methods of scoring in football _____

© 1997 Gage Educational Publishing Company

A. Use the dictionary samples to answer the questions below.

tux·e·do (tuk sē´dō) *n.* **1** a man's semiformal jacket for evening wear, usually black with satin or grosgrain lapels and made without tails; dinner jacket. **2** a suit of men's evening clothes including such a jacket. ⟨< *Tuxedo* Park, New York, where it is supposed to have been first worn⟩

twin (twin) *n.* **1** one of two children or animals born at the same time from the same mother **2** one of two persons or things very much or exactly alike in structure, appearance, etc.: *This table is the twin of one we have at home* –*adj.* being two persons or things very much or exactly alike; paired or matching: *twin houses, twin dresses.* –*v.* give birth to twins.

1. What part of speech is tuxedo? _____

2. How many definitions are given for tuxedo? _____

3. How many definitions are given for the noun twin? _____

4. Which word can be used as an adjective? _____

5. Which word comes from the name of a place in New York? _____

6. How many syllables are there in tuxedo? _____

   in twin? _____

7. What parts of speech is twin? _____

8. Underline the pair of words that could be guide words for the dictionary entries above.

   a. turtle / twill   **b.** twang / twist

   c. tusk / twirl   **d.** Tuscan / twig

B. Write the part of the book you would use to answer the following questions.

1. What is the name of Chapter 2? _____

2. Who wrote the book? _____

3. When was the book published? _____

4. Does the book have information on William Lyon Mackenzie? _____

C. Write the answers to the questions below.

1. How are books arranged on library shelves? _____

2. What are three ways of finding a book in a library catalogue? _____

3. Which of these methods would you use to locate a book by Yousuf Karsh? _____

D. On the first line, write the word you would look under in an encyclopedia to find an article on the topic. On the second line, write a possible cross-reference.

1. New Zealand _____ _____

2. New Brunswick _____ _____

3. palm trees _____ _____

E. Use the map to answer the questions.

City Park

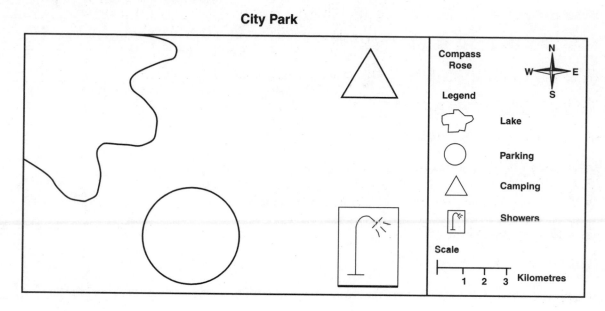

1. What direction is the lake from the camping area? _____

2. How far is parking from the camping area? _____

3. Which direction would you go to get to the camping area from the showers? _____

F. Use the thesaurus sample below to answer the questions.

> **sweet** *adj.* **syn.** pleasant, pure, fresh, sugary. **ant.** sour, acid, unripe, harsh

1. What is the entry word? _____

2. What are its synonyms? _____

3. Which word would you use in place of <u>charming</u>? _____

G. Write <u>encyclopedia</u>, <u>dictionary</u>, or <u>atlas</u> to show which source you would use to find the following information.

1. the definition of the word <u>realistic</u> _____

2. the location of the Gulf of St. Lawrence _____

3. the history of the Seven Years' War _____

A. Find the word <u>fallacy</u> in the dictionary. Then answer the questions.

1. Write the guide words from the page on which you found the entry for <u>fallacy</u>. _____

2. Write the word <u>fallacy</u> in syllables. _____

3. What part of speech is the word <u>fallacy</u>? _____

4. Write a sentence using the word <u>fallacy</u>. _____

5. Write two ways in which <u>fallacy</u> may be divided at the end of a writing line. _____

6. Write the respelling of <u>fallacy</u>. _____

B. Use a textbook with an index to answer the questions.

1. Copy the title from the title page. _____

2. Write the name(s) of the author(s). _____

3. What is the name of the publisher? _____

4. Name two other pieces of information that you can find on the copyright page. _____

C. Use the sample catalogue entry to answer the questions.

```
796.9640        CURLING
971W
                Weeks, Bob

                The Brier
                Toronto: Macmillan Canada, © 1995
                240 p.: 8 p. illus.
```

1. What kind of catalogue entry is this? _____

   a. title entry   **b.** subject entry   **c.** author entry

2. Who is the author of this book? _____

3. What is the title? _____

4. Who is the publisher? _____

5. Is the book illustrated? _____

6. What is the call number? _____

D. Use an encyclopedia to complete the following exercises.

1. What is the name of the encyclopedia you are using?

   _____

2. List the volume number in which you would find each topic in your encyclopedia.

   _____ **a.** Prince Edward Island   _____ **h.** Puerto Rico

   _____ **b.** North Carolina   _____ **i.** post office

   _____ **c.** Mount Everest   _____ **j.** Nelson Mandela

   _____ **d.** Niagara Falls   _____ **k.** country music

   _____ **e.** Mahatma Gandhi   _____ **l.** Thames River

   _____ **f.** New Zealand   _____ **m.** Indian Ocean

   _____ **g.** Olympic Games   _____ **n.** William Shakespeare

3. Look up each subject in your encyclopedia. Write a cross-reference for each subject.

   a. appaloosa _____

   b. Trafalgar Square _____

   c. canoe racing _____

   d. pirate _____

   e. library _____

   f. Stanley Livingston _____

E. Use the information in the chart to complete the bar graph. Then answer the questions below.

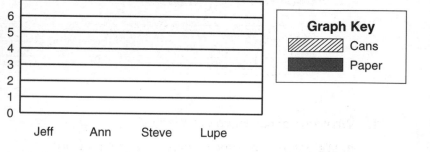

Recycling Chart

Person	Boxes of Cans	Boxes of Paper
Jeff	2	2
Ann	1	4
Steve	5	0
Lupe	4	2

1. Which two people recycled the same amount of paper? _____

2. Who recycled the most cans? _____

3. Who recycled the most materials altogether? _____

4. Is it easier to tell from the chart or the graph who recycled the most of each material? _____

Synonyms and Antonyms ■ On the line before each pair of words, write <u>S</u> if they are synonyms or <u>A</u> if they are antonyms.

1. _____ far, close

2. _____ discover, find

3. _____ shut, close

4. _____ mistake, error

5. _____ jagged, smooth

6. _____ yell, shout

7. _____ tall, short

8. _____ easy, simple

9. _____ together, apart

10. _____ honest, truthful

11. _____ clean, dirty

12. _____ tired, rested

13. _____ join, unite

14. _____ burn, scorch

15. _____ hit, strike

Homonyms ■ Underline the correct homonym in each sentence below.

1. He drove the wooden (steaks, stakes) into the ground.

2. We will (meet, meat) at Rosa's house tonight.

3. The audience thought the dull speaker was a (boar, bore).

4. The team (needs, kneads) more practice.

5. Homemade (bred, bread) smells wonderful when it is baking.

6. His (sun, son) plays on a professional basketball team.

7. The (plane, plain) couldn't take off in the heavy fog.

8. We (heard, herd) a strange noise outside the cabin.

Homographs ■ Write sentences for each of the homographs below. Use a different meaning in each sentence.

1. (set) _____

   (set) _____

2. (rose) _____

   (rose) _____

3. (fan) _____

   (fan) _____

4. (live) _____

   (live) _____

5. (tear) _____

   (tear) _____

Prefixes and Suffixes ■ Add a prefix or suffix to the underlined word in each sentence to form a new word that makes sense in the sentence. Write the new word in the blank.

1. I've always said that anything is <u>possible</u> if you always tell yourself that nothing is _____ .

2. That woman's business is a <u>success</u>, and she thanks her employees for making the past year the most

   _____ in the company's history.

3. It took many hours to <u>write</u> and then _____ the term paper to get it ready to hand in.

4. None of us were <u>certain</u> why we felt so _____ about which road to take.

Contractions and Compound Words ■ Write the two words that make up the contraction in each sentence. Then underline the compound word in each sentence, and draw a line between the two words that make up each compound word.

1. _____ _____ "Where's the airplane museum?" asked Anne.

2. _____ _____ "I think it's downtown," said Steve.

3. _____ _____ "Isn't that the headquarters of the parachute club?" asked Tim.

4. _____ _____ "Yes, they're in the same highrise," said Steve.

Connotation ■ Use the connotation of each underlined word below to answer the questions.

1. Which is more unattractive, a <u>plain</u> jacket or a <u>homely</u> jacket? _____

2. Would an <u>old</u> house or a <u>deteriorated</u> house probably be the better buy? _____

3. Did the critic like the movie more if he <u>raved</u> about it or <u>talked</u> about it? _____

4. Would a <u>fascinating</u> speaker or an <u>interesting</u> speaker be more enjoyable? _____

Idioms ■ Underline the idiom in each sentence. On the line after each sentence, explain what the idiom means. Use a dictionary if necessary.

1. We hit the sack early after our exhausting trip.

   _____

2. We were left high and dry on the island when our boat sank.

   _____

3. Our plans for the surprise party are up in the air.

   _____

4. I'm all thumbs when I try to build anything.

   _____

Types of Sentences ■ Before each sentence, write <u>D</u> for declarative, <u>IN</u> for interrogative, <u>IM</u> for imperative, <u>E</u> for exclamatory, or <u>X</u> if it is not a sentence. Punctuate each sentence correctly.

1. _____ I can't believe that fish got away _____

2. _____ Where do you think it went _____

3. _____ Under those rocks over there _____

4. _____ Have you ever lost a fish _____

5. _____ Many, many times _____

6. _____ I always throw the fish back _____

7. _____ Toss your line in over here _____

8. _____ Where's the best spot _____

9. _____ Near those trees in the middle _____

10. _____ I feel lucky _____

11. _____ Look at that splash _____

12. _____ I think it's a trout _____

Subjects and Predicates ■ Draw a line between the complete subject and the complete predicate in each sentence below. Underline the simple subject once and the simple predicate twice. Circle the sentence that is in inverted order.

1. Bicycling is a sport that people of all ages can enjoy.

2. Cyclists can learn hand signals and traffic rules.

3. Many cyclists wear special biking clothes and shoes.

4. A helmet is an important safety item.

5. Experts recommend that cyclists always ride with the flow of traffic.

6. City riders should learn how to ride in traffic.

7. All people who ride bicycles should obey the traffic laws.

8. Are you a careful and considerate cyclist?

Compound Subjects and Predicates ■ In each sentence below, draw a line between the complete subject and the complete predicate. Then write <u>CS</u> if the subject is compound or <u>CP</u> if the predicate is compound.

_____ 1. Joan Scott is concerned about car pollution and rides her bicycle to work.

_____ 2. Peter Scott and the two Scott children ride their bicycles to work and to school, too.

_____ 3. Joan and Peter run errands on their bicycles whenever possible.

_____ 4. The Scott children visit friends and go to after-school activities on their bicycles.

_____ 5. The Scott family helps save the environment and gets plenty of exercise.

_____ 6. Joan and Peter Scott think that bicycling is good for them and good for the earth.

Compound Sentences ■ Combine each pair of sentences below to form a compound sentence.

1. A bicycle safety course is offered at the recreation centre. The class is for children and adults together.

   _____

   _____

2. People are taught important traffic rules. They learn ways to prevent bicycle thefts.

   _____

   _____

3. Everyone must pass a final bicycling test. They will not get a certificate if they fail.

   _____

   _____

Correcting Run-on Sentences and Expanding Sentences ■ Correct the run-on sentences. Then expand each new sentence by adding details.

1. The cyclists rode, the rider in front led.

   a. _____

   b. _____

2. Two cyclists sped up, they pursued the leader.

   a. _____

   b. _____

3. A bicycle chain broke the leader fell behind.

   a. _____

   b. _____

4. Judges held stopwatches, riders crossed the finish line.

   a. _____

   b. _____

5. The race was over the spectators cheered.

   a. _____

   b. _____

Parts of Speech ■ Write the part of speech above each underlined word. Use the abbreviations in the box.

n. noun	adj. adjective	pp. prepositional phrase
int. interjection	adv. adverb	conj. conjunction
v. verb	prep. preposition	pron. pronoun

1. Mary swam in the lake until dark.

2. The fussy baby finally went to sleep.

3. Wow! That marble statue is really beautiful!

4. Nora and I worked late at the office.

5. Citizens of democratic countries exercise their right to vote in elections.

6. Pets are a source of companionship for many people.

7. She became the busiest supervisor at Hart Industries.

8. Recycling programs to protect our environment have become popular in most cities.

Verbs ■ Underline the correct verb to complete each sentence.

1. You (was, were) the first person hired.

2. She (will complete, completed) her driving course last week.

3. We have (saw, seen) all of her movies.

4. My friend (came, come) by train to visit me.

5. She hasn't (did, done) any preparation for her speech.

6. Who (drank, drunk) all the milk?

7. The volunteers haven't (ate, eaten) since breakfast.

8. We (rang, rung) the alarm at the first sign of danger.

9. Maria has (sang, sung) the national anthem at every game.

10. Have you (chose, chosen) your wedding dress yet?

11. The stereo was (broke, broken) when we bought it.

12. The passengers (grew, grown) tired of all the delays.

13. Sara has (went, gone) back to school.

14. Has Mr. Hall (gave, given) you the tickets yet?

15. Kara has (wrote, written) in her journal every day for a year.

Grammar and Usage ■ Fill in the blanks by supplying the word or words specified in parentheses.

Trees are important for _____ products and their benefits to the
(possessive pronoun)

environment. Wood _____ one of the main building supplies in the
(present tense of <u>be</u>)

world and an important fuel. Paper and paper products _____ from
(helping verb and verb)

wood pulp. Trees also _____ _____ nuts
(present tense verb)   (adjective)

and fruits for both _____ and humans.
(common noun)

One way _____ help the environment is by releasing oxygen
(plural of <u>tree</u>)

_____ the air. For instance, if a tree has _____
(preposition)   (past participle of <u>take</u>)

in sunlight and carbon dioxide, it _____ oxygen. Tree roots help
(future tense of <u>release</u>)

control erosion and flooding. Trees have always _____ homes
(past participle of <u>give</u>)

_____ shelter for _____ animals.
(conjunction)   (adjective)

Raccoons _____ , and other animals _____
(common noun)   (present tense verb)

their homes _____ trees.
(preposition)

_____ trees have lived and _____ for
(adjective)   (past participle of <u>grow</u>)

thousands of years and are many, many metres tall. The redwoods in California are some of the

_____ trees in the world. The tallest tree is 109 metres tall and lives
(superlative adjective)

_____ Humboldt National Forest. The _____
(preposition)   (superlative adjective)

living tree is a bristlecone pine that experts believe is _____
(adverb)

4600 years old.

© 1997 Gage Educational Publishing Company

Capitalization and End Punctuation ■ Circle each letter that should be capitalized. Write the capital letter above it. Add correct end punctuation to each sentence.

1. "how do you feel about cable television _____ " asked marie.

2. her friends looked at her in surprise _____

3. "it's wonderful _____ " said peter.

4. marie looked at peter and dino _____

5. "i like it," said dino, "but it costs too much to get everything _____ "

6. "i'd like to have the movie channels," marie said _____

7. "then why don't you just order them _____ " asked peter.

8. marie thought for a moment _____

9. "i think i will _____ " she exclaimed.

10. peter and dino laughed at marie's sudden enthusiasm _____

Punctuation and Capitalization ■ Circle each letter that should be capitalized below. Add commas, quotation marks, apostrophes, periods, colons, and hyphens where needed.

　　　　　　　　　　　　　　　　　　　122 park street e.
　　　　　　　　　　　　　　　　　　　lunenburg, ns b0j 3c4
　　　　　　　　　　　　　　　　　　　October 10, 1997

mr. marshal chase
3910 prairie avenue
flin flon, mb r8a 2m5

Dear mr. chase

　　thank you very much for your interest in my star gazing book a guide to the stars _____ i published it in september through a well known astronomy publisher the skys the limit press _____ according to my publisher, books will be available at bookstores this month _____

　　i have the answer to your question on how I do my research _____ i have a very powerful telescope that i use every day _____ i do most of my work at night between 1015 P.M. and 130 A.M. i find those to be the darkest hours out here in nova scotia _____ finally, i have a piece of advice for budding astronomers _____ always keep a journal of the stars you see each night and try to memorize their location _____ i always say to my students the skys the limit _____ good luck star gazing _____

　　　　　　　　　　　　　　　　　　　Sincerely,
　　　　　　　　　　　　　　　　　　　professor liz nelson

Commas and Quotation Marks ■ In the following example of a news conference, add commas and quotation marks where needed.

Ted Carter a United Nations spokesperson announced Many remote towns and villages in Mexico have been destroyed by a major earthquake and Canada and the United States are sending emergency relief. International troops will help with fires flooding and injuries resulting from the earthquake. The spokesperson further stated Colonel Marks commander of relief troops will oversee medical staff rescue crews and cleanup operations. Mr. Carter said The troops will provide medical supplies food water and temporary shelter for the earthquake victims. He ended his statement by saying The troops are preparing now and they should begin arriving in Mexico tomorrow morning. Mr. Carter then told the reporters that he would answer some questions.

Mr. Carter are any more countries involved in the relief efforts? asked Dorian Kramer reporter for the *Richland Register*.

Mr. Carter replied Yes. England France and Germany are also sending supplies and medical staff.

Pete Simmons CBC reporter asked How long will our troops be in Mexico?

Mr. Carter responded Well we are not sure but we expect the troops to be there for at least several weeks.

Jacinta Kareem *Up-Date* magazine reporter asked How many deaths and injuries have been reported?

We do not have exact figures but we know there are many people hurt and missing said Mr. Carter.

Apostrophes, Colons, and Hyphens ■ Add apostrophes, colons, and hyphens where needed in the sentences.

1. The boys father didn't want them to stay home alone.

2. Of all the countries Ive visited, these countries scenery impressed me most England, France, and Switzerland.

3. The flowers petals werent as colourful as the pictures showed them to be.

4. The Montréal mayors speeches at the national mayors convention will be at these times 500 P.M., 730 P.M., and 900 P.M.

5. My houses roof wasnt damaged by hail, but other houses roofs were Jims roof, my father in laws roof, my cousins roof, and Ms. Browns roof.

6. Many children attend our public librarys childrens hour on Tuesdays from 900 A.M. to 1000 A.M.

7. The new stores advertisement said it specializes in mens and womens clothing, ladies jewellery, and perfumes from around the world.

8. The winners trophy will be awarded to one of the twenty two contestants.

Topic Sentences ■ Write a topic sentence for the paragraphs below. Name a possible audience for each paragraph.

1. All children and adults should learn basic first aid. Courses are offered through schools and community groups. You never know when you'll need to clean a wound or use a more difficult technique during an emergency. By knowing first aid, you'll always be prepared.

   Topic Sentence: _____

   Audience: _____

2. Butterflies and moths fly from flower to flower, looking for pollen. When they land on a flower, some of the sticky pollen rubs off on their legs. When they fly to another flower, it rubs off onto the new flower.

   Topic Sentence: _____

   Audience: _____

3. Many people walk or run to stay healthy. Others swim or play sports for exercise. Some people prefer indoor exercises, such as using exercise videos and machines.

   Topic Sentence: _____

   Audience: _____

Supporting Details ■ Underline the two sentences that contain details that support the topic sentence.

1. **Topic Sentence:** A meteor looks like a bright streak of light in the sky.

   a. A meteor leaves a trail of hot gas.

   b. A meteor blazes across the sky as it travels through space.

   c. I saw a meteor fall from the sky.

2. **Topic Sentence:** Ants are called social insects.

   a. Ants live together in colonies and help each other.

   b. Ants are pests, and they can ruin a picnic.

   c. Ants share their food and their work.

3. **Topic Sentence:** Alligators and crocodiles are alike in many ways.

   a. Alligators have wider heads and shorter jaws than crocodiles.

   b. They are both reptiles and have rough skin.

   c. Alligators and crocodiles live in and near the water.

Revising and Proofreading ■ Rewrite the paragraphs below. Correct the errors by following the proofreader's marks.

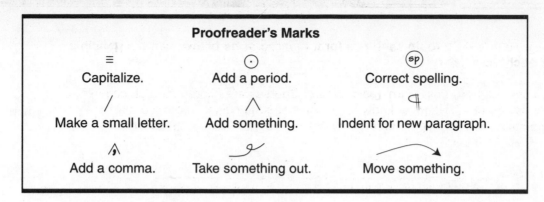

Proofreader's Marks

≡
Capitalize.

⊙
Add a period.

(sp)
Correct spelling.

/
Make a small letter.

∧
Add something.

⁋
Indent for new paragraph.

⁄∧
Add a comma.

☞
Take something out.

↷
Move something.

⁋ did you know that roughly three-quarters of the earth's fresh water is held not in rivers and lakes?

the water is held in glaciers, lage sheets of ice that form in high altitudes and polar regions such

as antarctica and Greenland their are between 70 000 and 200 000 glaicers in the world

⁋ as temperatures warm glaciers melt a little and move at a wrate that can't bee seen as they

move they sometimes freize and add to their mass before moving on they actually reshape

The land they pass over the most famus glaciers are in europe the best-known ones are

in the french and swiss alps

Using the Dictionary ▪ Use the dictionary samples to answer the questions.

firm (fėrm) *adj.* **1** not yielding easily to pressure or force **2** not easily moved or shaken; tightly fastened or fixed: *a tree firm in the earth.* **3** not easily changed; resolute; positive; determined: *a firm purpose.* –*n.* a company or partnership of two or more persons in business together. ⟨<L *firmus* firm⟩

fleet (flēt) *n.* **1** a group of warships under one command; navy: *the Canadian fleet.* **2** a group of boats, aircraft, automobiles, etc. moving or working together: *a fleet of trucks.* ⟨OE *flēot* ship, vessel < *flēotan* float⟩

1. Circle the letter of the guide words for the above entries.

    a. flag / fleece   **b.** float / flood   **c.** fire / flight

2. How many definitions are listed for firm? _____ fleet? _____

3. What part of speech is fleet? _____

4. How many syllables do fleet and firm have? _____

5. Write the respelling of fleet. _____ firm. _____

6. Which word came from the Latin word firmus? _____

Parts of a Book ▪ Write <u>title page</u>, <u>table of contents</u>, <u>index</u>, or <u>copyright page</u> to tell where each of the following would be found.

1. the page on which Lesson 12 begins _____

2. information about the Napoleonic Wars _____

3. where the book was published _____

4. the author of the book _____

Reference Sources ▪ Write <u>encyclopedia</u>, <u>dictionary</u>, <u>thesaurus</u>, or <u>atlas</u> to tell where you would find the following information.

1. the height of Mt. Everest _____

2. the definition of the word <u>astronomy</u> _____

3. the birthdate of John A. Macdonald _____

4. an antonym for the word <u>yell</u> _____

5. the location of the border between Canada and the United States _____

6. how earthquakes develop _____

7. a synonym for the word <u>carry</u> _____

8. the etymology of the word <u>pencil</u> _____